Grade 1

Treasures

Practice Book O

Macmillan McGraw-Hill

B

The *McGraw·Hill* Companies

Macmillan
McGraw-Hill

Published by Macmillan/McGraw-Hill, of McGraw-Hill Education, a division of The McGraw-Hill Companies, Inc., Two Penn Plaza, New York, New York 10121.

Printed in the United States of America

8 9 10 024 09 08 07

Contents

Unit I • All About Us

Unit 2 • Outside My Door

Unit 3 • Let's Connect

Unit 4 • Our Earth

Unit 5 • I Can Do It!

Unit 6 • Let's Discover

Name _____

Read the word. Circle the picture that it names.

1. cat

2. pan

3. man

4. sat

5. fan

6. Write a sentence using some of the words.

_____

_____

_____

 At Home: Have your child change the first letter of one of the words above to make a new word. Then have your child draw a picture of the new word.

Name _____

Complete each sentence.
Use one of the words in the box.

up	down	not	jump

_____

- - - - - - - - - - - - - -

1. I can _____.

_____

- - - - - - - - - - - - - -

2. The cat ran _____.

_____

- - - - - - - - - - - - - -

3. The cat is _____ little.

_____

- - - - - - - - - - - - - -

4. The dog ran _____.

5. Write your own sentence using a word from the box.

_____

- -

_____

© Macmillan/McGraw-Hill

At Home: Have your child create sentences using each word in the box.

As you read <u>Pam and Sam</u>, fill in the Character Chart.

Pam Can	Sam Can

How does the Character Chart help you remember the beginning, middle, and end of <u>Pam and Sam</u>?

© Macmillan/McGraw-Hill

At Home: Have your child use the chart to retell the story.

Pam and Sam • Book 1.1/Unit 1   3

Name _____

Look at the pictures. Read the story.

Nat is a cat.
Nat can go up.
Nat can go down.
Pam and Sam look for Nat.
Pam is sad.
Where is Nat?

Write <u>T</u> if the sentence is true.

Write <u>F</u> if the sentence is false.

____
- - - -

1. Nat is a cat. ____

____
- - - -

2. Nat can go up and down. ____

____
- - - -

3. Pam is sad. ____

____
- - - -

4. Nat is in the  . ____

____
- - - -

5. Nat is in the . ____

© Macmillan/McGraw-Hill

At Home: Have your child talk about all the things cats can do.

Circle the word that names each picture.
Then write the word.

1.

cat   cats

_____

- - - - - - - - - - - - -

_____

2.

man   map

_____

- - - - - - - - - - - - -

_____

3.

pan   pans

_____

- - - - - - - - - - - - -

_____

4.

rats   rat

_____

- - - - - - - - - - - - -

_____

5.

mat   mats

_____

- - - - - - - - - - - - -

_____

6.

can   cans

_____

- - - - - - - - - - - - -

_____

7.

fans   fan

_____

- - - - - - - - - - - - -

_____

8.

hat   hats

_____

- - - - - - - - - - - - -

_____

© Macmillan/McGraw-Hill

At Home: Have your child use some of the words on the page to write a sentence.

Pam and Sam • Book 1.1/Unit 1   5

As I read, I will pay attention to the punctuation.

09	"I can jump," said Frog. "I can jump up and down."
11	"I can jump," said Rabbit. "I can jump up
20	and down."
22	"I can jump, too!" said Kangaroo. "I can
30	jump up and down."
34	"I can not jump," said Little Bat.
41	"I can fly!" said Little Bat. 47

Comprehension Check

1. What can Frog, Rabbit, and Kangaroo do?

2. What can Little Bat do?

	Words Read	−	Number of Errors	=	Words Correct Score
First Read		−		=	
Second Read		−		=	

At Home: Help your child read the passage, paying attention to the goal at the top of the page.

Name _____

> **Photographs** are pictures that show people, animals, and things in real life.

Look at the picture.
Read the sentence that tells about the picture.

Look! My little cat is here.

Write your own sentence about the picture.

_____
- -
_____
- -
_____

At Home: Look through magazines for interesting photographs. Ask your child to tell a story about one of the photographs.

Pam and Sam • **Book 1.1/Unit 1**   **7**

Name _____

Look at each picture. Complete each sentence by using a word from the box.

hat	map	pan	ran	bat	mat

1. The cat is in the _____ .

_____

2. She sees the _____ .

_____

3. Sam _____ to the van.

_____   _____

4. The _____ is on the _____ .

_____

5. The man looks at the _____ .

At Home: Have your child look around the house for things that have the short *a* sound. Encourage your child to make up a silly story using some of these things.

Name _____

Say the name of each picture.
Circle the picture if you hear the sound of short <u>a</u>.

At Home: Have your child change the first letter of one of the words to make a new word. Then have him or her draw a picture of the new word.

Name _____

Fill in the sentences using the words in the box.

too	It	Yes	over

_____

1. _____ is in the box.

_____

2. _____, I can.

_____

3. It is _____ us.

4. You have fun,

_____

_____!

At Home: Play *I Spy* using the words *too, it, yes,* and *over:* For example: *I spy something **over** your head. I spy something you like to eat, **too.***

Name _____

As you read <u>I Can! Can You?</u>, fill in the Sequence Chart.

First

↓

Next

↓

Last

How does the Sequence Chart help you retell
<u>I Can! Can You?</u>

At Home: Have your child use the chart to retell the story.

Look at the pictures.
Write 1, 2, and 3 for each column of pictures to show the order in which things happen.

© Macmillan/McGraw-Hill

At Home: Ask your child to tell how he or she does a favorite activity. Help him or her to use the words *first*, *next*, and *last*.

Name _____

Circle the word that completes each sentence. Then write the word on the line.

1. Sam _____.

nap   naps

2. Sam and Pam _____.

play   plays

3. Pam can _____.

pack   packs

4. Pam _____ go with Sam.

can   cans

5. Pam _____ at Sam.

look   looks

© Macmillan/McGraw-Hill

At Home: Have your child write a sentence using one of the words.

I Can! Can You? • **Book 1.1/Unit 1**   13

As I read, I will pay attention to the punctuation.

	Is it fun to play tennis?
06	Yes! You can hit a ball over the net!
15	Is it fun to play soccer?
21	Yes! You can kick a ball.
27	Is it fun to play golf, too?
34	Yes! You can hit a ball. 40

Comprehension Check

1. Why is tennis fun?

2. Why is soccer fun?

	Words Read	−	Number of Errors	=	Words Correct Score
First Read		−		=	
Second Read		−		=	

At Home: Help your child read the passage, paying attention to the goal at the top of the page.

Labels give information about a picture.

Look at the picture. Read the labels.

hat

pack

bat

SAM

PAM

cap

Write the word that completes each sentence.

_____

- - - - - - - - - - - - -

1. The man has a _____.

_____

- - - - - - - - - - - - -

2. Pam has a _____.

_____

- - - - - - - - - - - - -

3. The cat has a _____.

_____

- - - - - - - - - - - - -

4. Sam has a _____.

At Home: Have your child think of other labels to add to each picture. Write the words next to the picture. Help your child to read the words.

Name _____

Circle the pictures that have the short <u>a</u> sound.
Then write the word on the line.

1

_____

2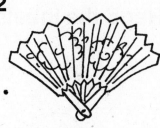

_____

3

_____

4

_____

5

_____

6

_____

7

_____

8

_____

9

_____

At Home: Ask your child to make up a story using some of the pictures on the page. Help your child to recognize any other words that have the short *a* sound.

Name _____

The letter **i** stands for the middle sound in **big** and **fin**.

Read the words in the box. Then write the word that names each picture.

| pig | kid | pin | sit |

1. _____

2. _____

3. _____

4. _____

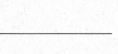 **At Home:** Have your child change the first letter of one of the words to make a new word. Then have your child draw a picture of the new word.

How You Grew • **Book 1.1/Unit 1**   **17**

Name ______________________________

Write the word from the box that completes each sentence. Circle the picture that goes with the sentence.

ride	be	ride	run

1. Nan will ______________ here.

2. My cat can ______________ here with me.

3. Nat can ______________ down to Mom.

4. I can ______________ with Nat.

At Home: Ask your child to choose a picture and make up a sentence using one of the words in the box.

Name _____

As you read <u>How You Grew</u>, fill in the Sequence Chart.

```
┌─────────────────────────────────────────────┐
│                                             │
│                  First                      │
│                                             │
└─────────────────────────────────────────────┘
                      ↓
┌─────────────────────────────────────────────┐
│                                             │
│                  Next                       │
│                                             │
└─────────────────────────────────────────────┘
                      ↓
┌─────────────────────────────────────────────┐
│                                             │
│                  Then                       │
│                                             │
└─────────────────────────────────────────────┘
                      ↓
┌─────────────────────────────────────────────┐
│                                             │
│                  Last                       │
│                                             │
└─────────────────────────────────────────────┘
```

**How does the Sequence Chart help you retell
<u>How You Grew</u>?**

 At Home: Have your child use the chart to retell the story.

Name _____

Look at the story pictures.
Read the sentences about the story.

 1.  2.  3.  4.

The ball is down.
My cat and I play ball.
My cat runs down, too.
My cat plays with a ball.

Write the sentences in the correct order on the lines.

_____

1. _____

_____

2. _____

_____

3. _____

_____

4. _____

© Macmillan/McGraw-Hill

At Home: Have your child tell you another story in correct time order about the boy and his cat.

Name _____

> Some words end in the same two consonants.
>
> bi**ll**   Ja**zz**   pa**ss**

Read each sentence.
Underline the word that ends with the same two consonants. Write the word on the line.

1. Matt runs to his little cat.

_____

- - - - - - - - - - - - - - -

_____

2. Pam rides to the hill.

_____

- - - - - - - - - - - - - - -

_____

3. I kiss my Dad.

_____

- - - - - - - - - - - - - - -

_____

4. The mitt is on the ride.

_____

- - - - - - - - - - - - - - -

_____

© Macmillan/McGraw-Hill

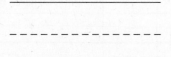

At Home: Have your child make up a sentence with another word that ends with the same two consonants. Then have your child draw a picture to illustrate the sentence.

Name _____

As I read, I will pay attention to patterns in the story.

	This boy is 4. He can jump.
06	This girl will be 6. What can she do?
14	She can ride the bus to school.
21	This boy will be 12. What can he do?
29	He can ride his bike fast. 35

Comprehension Check

1. Who can ride the bus to school?

2. What can the boy who is 12 do?

	Words Read	–	Number of Errors	=	Words Correct Score
First Read		–		=	
Second Read		–		=	

At Home: Help your child read the passage, paying attention to the goal of the top of the page.

Name _____

The **title** of a book is the name of the book.
The **author** of a book writes the story.
The **illustrator** makes the pictures.

Look at the book cover. Answer the questions.

1. Who wrote the book?

_____

- - - - - - - - - - - - - - - -

_____

Title

Picture

Author

Illustrator

2. Who made the picture?

_____

- - - - - - - - - - - - - - - -

_____

3. What is the title of the book?

_____

- -

_____

4. What picture is on the cover?

_____

- -

_____

At Home: Have your child identify the title, author, and
illustrator of a favorite book. Talk about the book together.

Write a word from the box to finish the sentence.

| lid | pig | dig | wig | hid | bib |

_____
- - - - - - - - -

1. Pat likes her _____.

_____
- - - - - - - - -

2. He is a big _____.

_____
- - - - - - - - -

3. The _____ is on the pan.

_____
- - - - - - - - -

4. Sam can _____ in it.

_____
- - - - - - - - -

5. Jan _____ it.

_____
- - - - - - - - -

6. The cat has the _____.

At Home: Have your child make up a story using some of the words from the box.

Name _____

Sometimes consonants form a **blend**. You can hear each consonant sound in a **consonant blend**.

Read the word. Write the word.
Circle the picture that it names.

I. g r a s s

_____

- - - - - - - - - - - - - - - - - - -

_____

2. t r a c k

_____

- - - - - - - - - - - - - - - - - - -

_____

3. F r a n

_____

- - - - - - - - - - - - - - - - - - -

_____

4. b r i c k

_____

- - - - - - - - - - - - - - - - - - -

_____

5. c r i b

_____

- - - - - - - - - - - - - - - - - - -

_____

At Home: Play a game with your child to name other words that begin with the *br, tr, fr, cr,* and *gr* sound. One suggestion is to name food items that you see in the kitchen.

Pet Tricks • **Book 1.1/Unit 1** **25**

Write a word from the box to complete each sentence. Some words may be used more than once.

come	good	on	that

_____
- - - - - - - - - - - - - - - -
1. Rags can _____ with me.

_____
- - - - - - - - - - - - - -
2. Can Rags _____ in?

_____
- - - - - - - - - - - - - -
3. Rags is a _____ pet.

_____
- - - - - - - - - - - - - - -
4. Is _____ for Rags?

_____
- - - - - - - - - - - - - -
5. Rags is _____ my .

At Home: Ask your child to make up a sentence for each word in the box.

As you read <u>Pet Tricks</u>, fill in the Setting Chart.

Setting	What the Characters Do There

How does the Setting Chart help you retell <u>Pet Tricks</u>?

 At Home: Have your child use the chart to retell the story.

Name _____

> The **characters** are the people or animals in a story.
>
> The **setting** is where the story happens.

Amusement Park

Answer the questions about the characters and the setting.

_____

_____

1. Where are the cats? _____

2. Is the cat sad? _____

3. Do the cats like to play? _____

At Home: Ask your child to tell you more about the characters and where the story takes place.

© Macmillan/McGraw-Hill

Name _____

When **'s** is added to a word, it means that something belongs to that person or thing.

Circle the correct word and write it on the line.

1. This is _____ pet.

   Fran   Fran's

2. This is _____ bag.

   Gram's   Gram

3. This is the _____ trap.

   crab   crab's

4. This is _____ cat.

   Mr. Tran   Mr. Tran's

5. This is _____ crib.

   Jim's   Jim

At Home: Have your child draw a picture to illustrate one of the sentences.

As I read, I will pay attention to the punctuation.

Rosa got a new puppy.
05 | "That is a good puppy," said Rosa.
12 | Rosa set a bowl on the floor.
19 | "Come and drink," said Rosa.
24 | Rosa set a dish on the floor.
31 | "Come and eat," said Rosa.
36 | Rosa got a leash for the puppy. 43

Comprehension Check

1. Why do you think Rosa put a leash on the puppy?

2. What things does a puppy need?

	Words Read	–	Number of Errors	=	Words Correct Score
First Read		–		=	
Second Read		–		=	

At Home: Help your child read the passage, paying attention to the goal at the top of the page.

Name _____

A **list** is a series of things written in order.

Pets can:

1.

2.

3.

4.

Read the question. Draw a line to the answer.

1. What pet likes to nap?

2. What pet can sit?

3. What pet can wag?

4. What pet likes to play?

 **At Home:** If you have a pet, make a list with your child of the things you do to take care of it. If you do not have a pet, ask you child to make a list of pets he or she would like to have.

Look at each picture.
Write the word that describes the picture.

grass	crab	crib	trip	brick

1. _____

2. _____

3. _____

4. _____

5. _____

Write a sentence using one of the words in the box.

_____

_____

At Home: Have your child name any toys or things that can be seen from a window and start with an *r* blend.

> Sometimes consonants form a **blend**. You can hear each consonant sound in a **final blend**.
>
> ha**nd** pa**st**

Say the word. Draw a line under the final blend. Write the final blend on the line. Circle the picture.

1. a n t _____ _____

2. l i s t _____ _____

3. b a n d _____ _____

4. r i n k _____ _____

© Macmillan/McGraw-Hill

 **At Home:** Have your child identify some things in your home or community that end with each blend: *nd, st, nt,* or *nk.*

Name _____

Use a word from the box to complete each sentence.

very	help	use	now

1. Tom can _____ Nan ride.

2. Look! What she did is _____ good.

3. Sam and Matt go up and down _____.

4. Dick and Nan _____ the big pan.

At Home: Ask your child to say a sentence using a word from the box. Then draw a picture to illustrate the sentence.

© Macmillan/McGraw-Hill

As you read <u>Soccer</u>, fill in the Author's Purpose Chart.

Clue	Clue

Author's Purpose

How does the Author's Purpose Chart help you
understand the story <u>Soccer</u>?

At Home: Have your child use the chart to retell the story.

Soccer • **Book 1.1/Unit 1**   35

Some authors write to tell a story. Some authors write to tell about real people or things.

Read the sentences. Choose the author's purpose.

1. Ben the cat likes to play with a pink ball. Look at Ben run! Look at Ben go!

   ○ tell a story

   ○ tell about real people or things

2. An ant can walk. A shark can swim. A cat can run. A kangaroo can hop.

   ○ tell a story

   ○ tell about real people or things

3. Where is the band? The band is not here! "What will we do now?" said Crab. "We will play!" said Ant.

   ○ tell a story

   ○ tell about real people or things

4. Dogs can jump up and down. Dogs can sit. Dogs can run fast. Dogs can play with you.

   ○ tell a story

   ○ tell about real people or things

At Home: Have your child draw a picture for the other sentence group. Talk about the picture.

Name _____

Read each sentence. Then read the words under each sentence. Write the correct word on the line.

1. We like to play in the

_____

- - - - - - - - - - - - - -

_____ .

sun   sand   lot

_____

- - - - - - - - - - - - - -

2. The _____ is very big.

rat   rink   rim

_____

- - - - - - - - - - - - - -

3. Pam and Nat look here _____ .

lap   let   last

_____

- - - - - - - - - - - - - -

4. Nan and I look at a _____ .

tent   help   use

© Macmillan/McGraw-Hill

At Home: Have your child use one word with a CVCC letter pattern in a sentence.

Soccer • **Book 1.1/Unit 1**   **37**

As I read, I will pay attention to the punctuation.

	Look at the sand. We can not use the sand.
10	We can help. We can pick up.
17	Look! The sand is very clean. We can use the
27	sand now.
29	Look at the park. We can not use the park.
39	We can help! We can pick up. 46

Comprehension Check

1. What is wrong with the sand and the park?

2. What can the children do to help?

	Words Read	–	Number of Errors	=	Words Correct Score
First Read		–		=	
Second Read		–		=	

At Home: Help your child read the passage, paying attention to the goal at the top of the page.

Words in a poem often **rhyme.** Rhyming words begin with different sounds and end with the same sound.

m**ap**   t**ap**

Read the poem. Write the rhyming words on the line. Circle the same sound in each word.

Where Did the Ball Go?

1. Pam can kick.
Now she is very quick.

_____
- -
_____

2. Where will the ball land?
Will it sink in the sand?

_____
- -
_____

3. Now it will fall.
It is just a red ball.

_____
- -

At Home: Have your child make up two more rhyming lines for this poem.

Name _____

Look at the picture. Write sentences about the picture. Use a word with a <u>final blend</u> in each sentence.

| ant | band | sand | fast | wind | sink |

_____

- -

See the _____

_____

- -

Look at the _____

_____

- -

What _____?

© Macmillan/McGraw-Hill

At Home: Have your child develop a scene of another place. He or she can draw it and then write sentences about it that include final blends.

Name _____

Circle the word that tells about the picture. Then write the word on the line.

1. _____

jump   run

2. _____

up   down

3. _____

go   come

4. _____

good   sad

5. _____

in   on

6. _____

help   sit

© Macmillan/McGraw-Hill

Name _____

Match each sentence to the picture that it explains.

1. **It** is **too** little.

a.

2. Bill can **ride now**.

b.

3. **That** is **not** Ann's cat.

c.

4. **Yes,** Jack can **use help.**

d.

5. Jill can do **very good** tricks.

e.

6. Pam can **run** and **jump.**

f.

Name _____

> The letter **o** stands for the middle sound in **log**.

Blend the sounds and say the word. Then write the word and circle the picture.

1. p o t _____

2. h o g _____

3. b o x _____

4. t o p _____

5. f o x _____

 At Home: Have your child change the first letter of one of the words to make a new word.

© Macmillan/McGraw-Hill

Write the word that completes each sentence.

one	two	does	her	They

1. This mom has _____ cat.

2. She naps with _____ mom.

3. This mom has _____ dogs.

4. _____ play with mom.

5. What _____ this mom have?

At Home: Have your child answer question 5 and then write a sentence that tells about it.

© Macmillan/McGraw-Hill

Name _____

**As you read <u>Animal Moms and Dads</u>, fill in
the Main Idea and Details Web.**

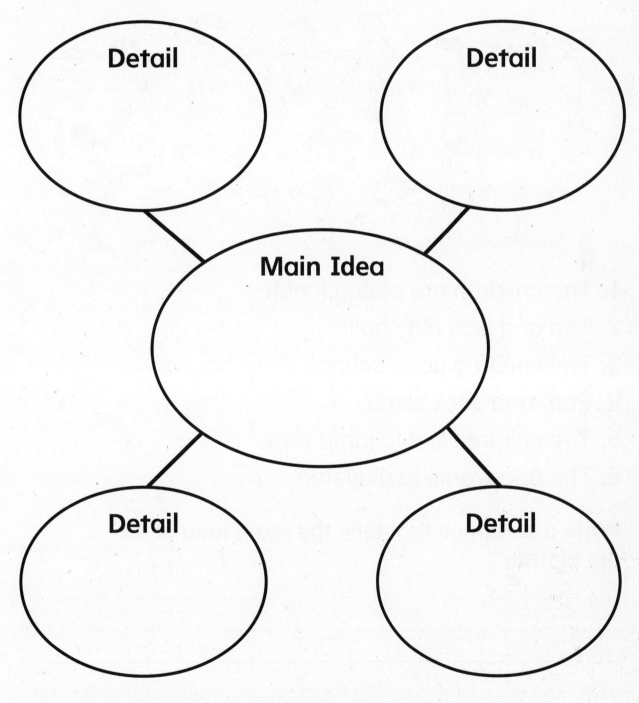

How does the Main Idea and Details Web help you
retell <u>Animal Moms and Dads</u>?

At Home: Have your child use the web to retell the story.

Animal Moms and Dads
Book I.2/Unit 2

45

Look at the picture. Circle all the sentences that tell about the picture.

1. The children are eating lunch.

2. Kim and Bob play ball.

3. The children go to school.

4. Pam and Jack climb.

5. The children like to jump rope.

6. The dog wants to play, too.

Write a sentence that tells the main idea of the picture.

_____

- - - - - - - - - - - - - - - - -

_____

_____

- - - - - - - - - - - - - - - - -

_____

© Macmillan/McGraw-Hill

 At Home: Have your child look in magazines for pictures that show people at work or play. Ask your child to tell the main idea of each picture.

You can add **-ed** to some action words to tell what someone or something did.   **walk + ed = walked**

Circle the word that completes the sentence. Then write the word.

_____

1. I _____ my bag.

      rocked   packed

_____

2. Dad _____ the  .

      locked   packed

_____

3. Bob _____ up the dog.

      picked   licked

_____

4. The cat _____ up on my lap.

      jumped   picked

_____

5. Pat _____ the  .

      rocked   kicked

© Macmillan/McGraw-Hill

At Home: Help your child to use the first three words in sentences.

Name _____

As I read, I will pay attention to patterns in the story.

	Look at the big bear. Look at her cubs.
9	What can the two cubs do? They can play.
18	They can look for food to eat.
25	The cubs can rest. They take a long nap.
34	The cubs can play on the rocks. 41

Comprehension Check

1. What are cubs?

2. What can the cubs do?

	Words Read	−	Number of Errors	=	Words Correct Score
First Read		−		=	
Second Read		−		=	

At Home: Help your child read the passage, paying attention to the goal at the top of the page.

Rhythmic patterns are sounds and words that repeat to give a poem a beat.

Read the poem.

One little cat,
Sat on a mat.
She did not run,
She did not pat.

One little frog,
Sat on a log.
He did not jump,
He did not jog.

1. Write three words that rhyme in the first verse.

_____   _____   _____

2. Write three words that rhyme in the second verse.

_____   _____   _____

3. Underline three words that repeat in the first verse.

4. Underline three words that repeat in the second verse.

At Home: With your child, clap out the beat for each verse of the poem.

Name _____

Read the question. Look at the picture. Write the word.

1. Is this a cat or a cot?

_____

- - - - - - - - - - - - - -

_____

2. Is this a crib or a crab?

_____

- - - - - - - - - - - - - -

_____

3. Is this a fan or a fin?

_____

- - - - - - - - - - - - - -

_____

4. Is this a mop or a map?

_____

- - - - - - - - - - - - - -

_____

5. Is this a sock or a sack?

_____

- - - - - - - - - - - - - -

_____

6. Is this a pin or a pan?

_____

- - - - - - - - - - - - - -

_____

At Home: Have your child write sentences using the short *o* words on the page.

Name _____

Use the words from the box to name each picture.

| dress | net | cent | leg | bed | ten |

1. _____

2.  _____

3. _____

4.  _____

5. **10** _____

6. _____

At Home: Have your child create two sentences using words in the box.

Name _____

Write a word from the box to complete each sentence.

Who	some	of	No	eat

1. Did you get _____ for me?

2. _____ can get the down?

3. The bag _____ is in the box.

4. _____, I can not ride a .

5. Can I _____ with you?

At Home: Ask your child to write another sentence using one of the words in the box.

© Macmillan/McGraw-Hill

Name _____

As you read <u>Little Red Hen</u>, fill in the Retelling Chart.

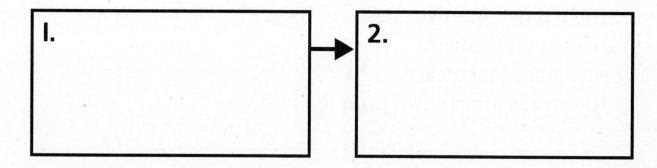

Little Red Hen

1.	2.

3.	4.

5.	6.

**How does the Retelling Chart help you remember
<u>Little Red Hen</u>?**

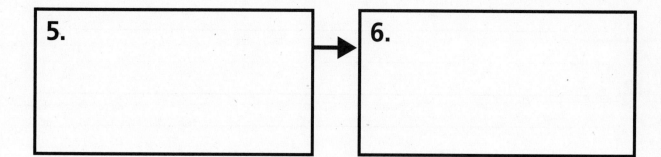

At Home: Have your child use the chart to retell the story.

When you **retell** a story, you tell only the important parts.

Read each story. Write a new sentence that tells only the important parts. Then draw a picture.

The red hen has two eggs.
She sits on the nest.
Now the eggs crack.
The chicks jump down from the nest.

_____

1. _____

Jen has a pet cat.
Greg has a pet dog.
Jen's cat jumps on Greg's dog.
The dog does not run.
Greg's dog licks Jen's cat.

_____

2. _____

_____

_____

At Home: Ask your child to tell you what happened after school.

Name _____

A **contraction** is a short form of two words. An **apostrophe (')** takes the place of the missing letters.   can + not = **can't**

| didn't | can't | doesn't | isn't |

Write the contractions.

_____

1. does not _____

_____

2. did not _____

_____

3. can not _____

_____

4. is not _____

5. Write a sentence using a contraction from the box.

_____

_____

At Home: Have your child write a sentence using another contraction in the box.

As I read, I will pay attention to questions in the passage.

10	Look at the farm. What can you get from a farm?
11	Look at the cows. We get milk from the cows.
21	Who will have some of the milk?
28	Look at the hen. We get eggs from the hen.
38	Who will eat some of the eggs? 45

Comprehension Check

1. What do we get from cows?

2. What do we get from hens?

	Words Read	–	Number of Errors	=	Words Correct Score
First Read		–		=	
Second Read		–		=	

At Home: Help your child read the passage, paying attention to the goal at the top of the page.

Name _____

A **diagram** is a picture that shows the parts of something.

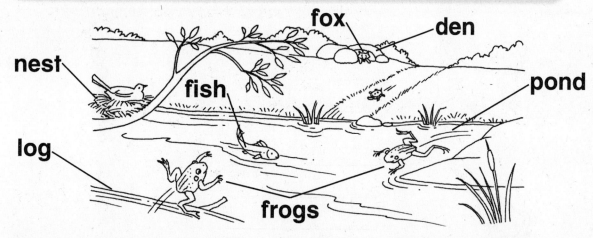

nest

fox   den

fish   pond

log

frogs

Write a word from the diagram to complete each sentence.

1. Two frogs jump in the _____.

2. The _____ is in the .

3. A fox is in a _____.

4. A _____ is in the pond.

© Macmillan/McGraw-Hill

At Home: Have your child think of other animals to add to the diagram. Then help your child write the labels on the diagram.

Use the words from the box to name each picture.

bell	pond	vest	dog	cob	Kent

1.  _____

2. _____

3. _____

4.  _____

5. _____

6.  _____

At Home: Have your child use two of the words in a sentence.

Name _____

> Read each word. Listen to the sounds **sh** and **th** stand for.
>
> pa**th**   **th**ink   **sh**ip   **sh**op   di**sh**   ba**th**

Use the words in the box to name each picture. Then circle the letters that stand for the sounds <u>sh</u> and <u>th</u>.

1.  _____

2. _____

3.  _____

4.  _____

5. _____

 At Home: Have your child write a sentence with one or more words that begin or end with *sh* or *th*.

A Prairie Dog Home • Book 1.2/Unit 2   59

Name _____

Write a word from the box to complete each sentence. Match each sentence to the correct picture.

live	into	out	many

1. The _____ in a nest.

2. They run _____ the .

3. We don't go _____ in the  .

4. He has _____ in his bag.

At Home: Ask your child to write a sentence using one or two of the words in the box.

Name _____

**As you read <u>A Prairie Dog Home</u>, fill in the
Main Idea and Details Web.**

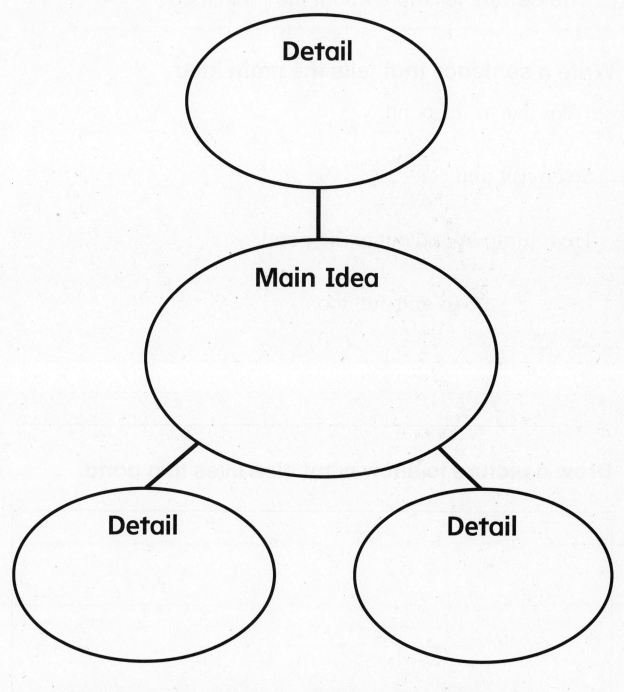

Detail

Main Idea

Detail

Detail

How does the Main Idea and Details Web help you
better understand <u>A Prairie Dog Home</u>?

At Home: Have your child use the web to retell the story.

A Prairie Dog Home • **Book 1.2/Unit 2** 61

© Macmillan/McGraw-Hill

The **main idea** tells what the story is about.

The **details** tell more about the main idea.

Write a sentence that tells the main idea.

Frogs live in the pond.

So do fish and  .

Frogs jump in and out of the pond.

 go in and out, too.

_____

- -

_____

Draw a picture to show what else lives in a pond.

At Home: Have your child tell you about a favorite story or TV show. Ask about the main idea and a detail that supports the main idea.

You can add **-ing** to some action words.

Add -ing to the words in the box.

look _____   jump _____

play _____   wash _____

Complete the sentences with the words you wrote.

1. Beth is _____ a big dog.

2. They are _____ for a lost cat.

3. I am _____ with a little ship.

4. We are _____ up and down.

At Home: Have your child write a sentence using a word ending with *-ing*.

A Prairie Dog Home • **Book 1.2/Unit 2**   63

As I read, I will pay attention to questions in the passage.

	Where do birds live? Birds live in many places.
9	This bird lives in a park. It hops in the grass.
20	The bird used twigs to make a nest.
28	Look into the nest. What do you see?
36	This bird lives in the woods. It will peck a
46	hole in the tree. 50

Comprehension Check

1. Where do some birds live?

2. What do some birds use to make a nest?

	Words Read	–	Number of Errors	=	Words Correct Score
First Read		–		=	
Second Read		–		=	

At Home: Help your child read the passage, paying attention to the goal at the top of the page.

Name _____

> A **dictionary** gives the meaning of words.

> **grand** very big   **mend** to fix
>
> **ship** a big    **lamb** a little

Write a dictionary word to complete each sentence.

1. The _____ likes to run and play.

2. The ship is very _____.

3. I have to _____ my pants.

4. A _____ is too big for a pond.

Write a new sentence for one of the words.

5. _____

At Home: Together with your child, look up these words in the dictionary. Read the meanings and sample sentences. Ask your child to use one of the words in a sentence.

Use the words in the box to name each picture.
Underline the letters that stand for the sounds <u>sh</u> and <u>th</u>.

| bath | thin | shell | fish | pen | lock |

1.  _____

2. 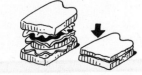 _____

3. _____

Circle the letters that stand for the short <u>e</u> and <u>o</u> sound.

4. _____

5. _____

6. _____

At Home: Have your child use two of the words in sentences.

Name _____

The letter **u** stands for the middle sound in **bus.**

Circle the word that names each picture.
Then write the word.

1.

   bun   big

   _____

2.

   pot   pup

   _____

3.

   ten   tub

   _____

4.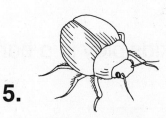

   sun   sad

   _____

5.

   bat   bug

   _____

6.

   drip   drum

   _____

At Home: Have your child use some of the words to write a sentence.

Write a word from the box to complete each sentence.

| make | want | under | Put | show | Three |

_____
- - - - - - - - - - - - - - - -
1. _____ on a hat.

_____
- - - - - - - - - - - - - - -
2. Sit _____ the tent.

_____
- - - - - - - - - - - - - - - -
3. Come see the _____!

_____
- - - - - - - - - - - - - - -
4. _____ kids play in a band.

_____
- - - - - - - - - - - - - - -
5. You will _____ to see it.

_____
- - - - - - - - - - - - - - -
6. It will _____ you jump up and down.

At Home: Ask your child to draw a picture to illustrate two of the sentences.

© Macmillan/McGraw-Hill

Name _____

As you read <u>The Fun Kids' Band</u>, fill in the Retelling Chart.

The Fun Kids' Band

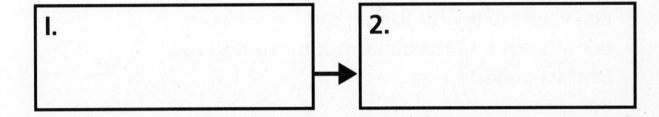

1.   →   2.

3.   →   4.

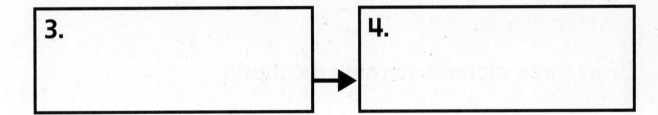

5.   →   6.

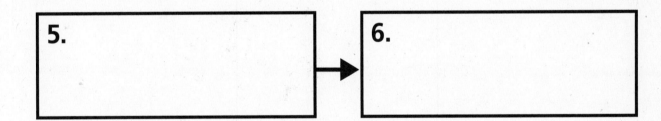

7.   →   8.

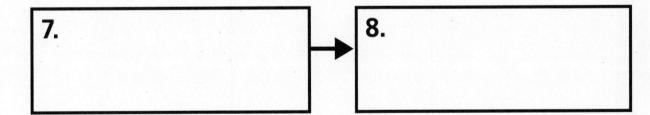

© Macmillan/McGraw-Hill

How does the Retelling Chart help you visualize what happens in <u>The Fun Kids' Band</u>?

At Home: Have your child use the chart to retell the story.

The Fun Kids' Band • **Book 1.2/Unit 2**   69

When you **retell** a story, you tell only the important parts.

Read the story. Then look at it again. Underline the sentences that retell the story.

Ben wants to use his fishing rod.

Ben sits down at the pond with his fishing rod.

Ben sits and sits.

Ben sees a frog.

Ben sees a bug.

At last Ben gets a fish!

Draw three pictures to retell the story.

At Home: Ask your child to pick a favorite fairy tale or folk tale and retell it. Remind your child to include only the important parts.

A **contraction** is a short form of two words. An **apostrophe** (') takes the place of one or more letters.

he's	it's	let's	she's	that's

Read each sentence. Then write the contraction for the underlined words.

1. Mom said <u>she is</u> going with us. _____

2. <u>That is</u> a big truck! _____

3. <u>Let us</u> run and jump. _____

4. Ted said <u>he is</u> playing the drum. _____

5. <u>It is</u> a dull rug. _____

At Home: Have your child write a sentence using one of the contractions.

The Fun Kids' Band • Book 1.2/Unit 2　71

As I read, I will pay attention to the dialogue.

	Meg, Jim, and Dan sat under a tree.
8	Dan's little sister sat under the tree, too.
16	Jim asked,
18	"What do you want to do?"
24	Meg said, "I want to put on a show. Do you
35	want to help me?"
39	Jim and Dan said, "Yes!" 44

Comprehension Check

1. What do the children want to do?

2. What do you need to put on a show?

	Words Read	–	Number of Errors	=	Words Correct Score
First Read		–		=	
Second Read		–		=	

© Macmillan/McGraw-Hill

At Home: Help your child read the passage, paying attention to the goal at the top of the page.

Directions are the steps that you follow to make or do something.

Make a Fun Box.

1. Get an egg carton.

2. Cut the top.

3. Give it a fun look.

4. Put in stuff.

1. What will you make? _____

2. What will you use? _____

3. What will you do with the top? _____

4. What will you do last? _____

At Home: Have your child make a fun box at home by following the directions on the page.

Circle the word that names each picture.
Then write the word.

1.

bag   beg

_____

- - - - - - - - - - -

_____

2.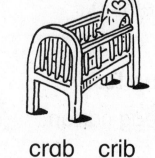

crab   crib

_____

- - - - - - - - - - -

_____

3.

ship   shop

_____

- - - - - - - - - - -

_____

4.

sock   sack

_____

- - - - - - - - - - -

_____

5.

duck   dock

_____

- - - - - - - - - - -

_____

6.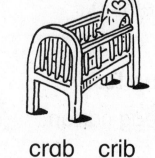

net   nut

_____

- - - - - - - - - - -

_____

At Home: Have your child use two or more of the words in sentences.

Name _____

Blend the first two letters to read each word.

flag   **cl**ap   **bl**ack   **bl**ock   **cl**ip   **cl**ock

Use the words in the box to name each picture.

1. _____

2. _____

3. _____

4. _____

5. _____

6. _____

At Home: Have your child find two more words that start with the *l* blends.

On My Way to School
Book 1.2/Unit 2

75

Read each sentence. Write a word from the box to complete the sentence.

away	late	school	today	way	Why

1. If the bus does not come, I will be _____.

2. _____ did the bus go in the mud?

3. This is the _____ to play.

4. We put the blocks _____.

5. I have to go to _____ now.

6. We can not play _____.

At Home: Have your child write a sentence using two of the words from the page.

Name _____

As you read <u>On My Way to School</u>, fill in the Sequence Chart.

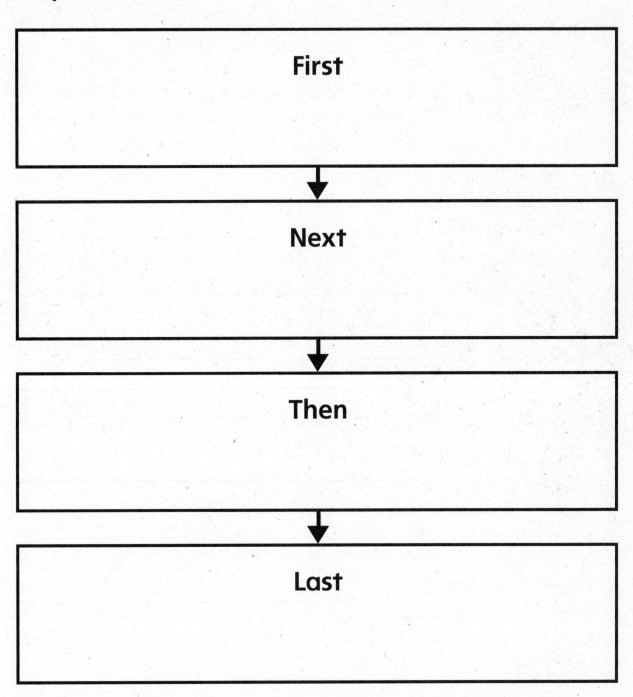

First

Next

Then

Last

How does the Sequence Chart help you visualize what happens in <u>On My Way to School</u>?

At Home: Have your child use the chart to retell the story.

On My Way to School
Book 1.2/Unit 2
77

Name _____

Look at the pictures. Write what happens in each picture.

1.

First, _____

Next, _____

Last, _____

2.

First, _____

Next, _____

Last, _____

© Macmillan/McGraw-Hill

At Home: Have your child draw a picture of what might happen next in one of the picture stories above, and then write a sentence about the picture.

Name _____

Circle the word that names each picture. Then write the word.

1.

clam   clip

_____

- - - - - - - - - - -

_____

2.

flag   flat

_____

- - - - - - - - - - -

_____

3.

clap   clip

_____

- - - - - - - - - - -

_____

4.

sled   slip

_____

- - - - - - - - - - -

_____

5.

clam   club

_____

- - - - - - - - - - -

_____

6.

plum   glad

_____

- - - - - - - - - - -

_____

At Home: Browse with your child through a favorite
storybook, and find two more words with the CCVC pattern.

As I read, I will pay attention to the punctuation.

	Elephant sat up. He looked at the clock.
8	"Oh no! I will be late for school!"
16	Elephant got dressed. He got his books. He got
25	his lunch. He put them in his blue backpack.
34	Elephant ran down the street. On the way,
42	he saw Bear. 45

Comprehension Check

1. What is the problem?

2. What does Elephant do to get ready for school?

	Words Read	–	Number of Errors	=	Words Correct Score
First Read		–		=	
Second Read		–		=	

© Macmillan/McGraw-Hill

At Home: Help your child read the passage, paying attention to the goal at the top of the page.

Name _____

A **sign** uses words or pictures to tell you what to do.

Circle the word that completes each sentence.

1. When you see , you _____.

                           stop   go

2. When you see , you _____.

                           stop   go

3. To play on the _____, we go to the .

                beds   swings

4. We _____ in the .

    run   eat

Color the traffic light with red, yellow, and green.
Put a ✔ next to the color that tells you to go.
Put an X next to the color that tells you to stop.

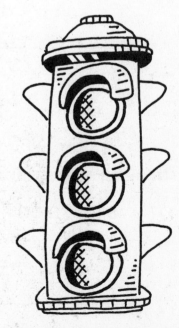

At Home: Talk about common signs that you and your child see in the neighborhood. Have your child draw a sign, and tell what it means.

Circle the word that tells about each picture.
Then write the word.

1.

plug   plum

_____

- - - - - - - - - - - - - - -

_____

2.

black   block

_____

- - - - - - - - - - - - - - -

_____

3.

clam   clock

_____

- - - - - - - - - - - - - - -

_____

4.

clip   clap

_____

- - - - - - - - - - - - - - -

_____

5.

slip   sled

_____

- - - - - - - - - - - - - - -

_____

6.

flop   flag

_____

- - - - - - - - - - - - - - -

_____

At Home: Have your child draw a picture of another word that begins with *pl, cl, sl, fl,* or *bl.* Then help your child label it.

Write the word that completes each sentence.

1. They _____ in a den.

        live   glad

2. Tom can _____ his hat on.

        cut   put

3. The frog jumps _____ the pond.

        out   into

4. My _____ dogs sit in the sun.

        two   does

5. _____ gets on the bus last?

        Who   Why

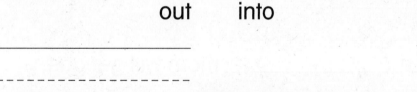

6. They can tell the _____ to go.

        way   ran

Name _____

Write a word from the box to complete each sentence.

late	her	show	today	make	some

1. We want to shop for socks _____.

2. I will _____ you the way.

3. Jen and _____ mom will get gas.

4. They can _____ a hat.

5. I can't be _____ for school.

6. I see _____ of the kids at the bus stop.

Name _____

Look at the word **gate.** The letters **a** and **e** stand for the **long a** sound you hear.

g **a** t e

Circle the word that names the picture. Write the word on the line.

1.

   cap   cape

   _____

   - - - - - - - - - - - - - -

   _____

2.

   tape   tap

   _____

   - - - - - - - - - - - - - -

   _____

3.

   pane   pan

   _____

   - - - - - - - - - - - - - -

   _____

4.

   man   mane

   _____

   - - - - - - - - - - - - - -

   _____

5.

   rat   rate

   _____

   - - - - - - - - - - - - - -

   _____

6.

   mate   mat

   _____

   - - - - - - - - - - - - - -

   _____

At Home: Write the words *rat* and *cap* and have your child read them. Add an *e* on the end of each word. Talk about how the words changed.

Write the words from the box to complete the letter.

> Oh   pull   Could   All   walk   Hello

_____

_____ Kate,

_____ you come on a _____

_____

with me? We could _____ our wagon.

_____ our pals could come. _____,
it will be fun!

From,

Jake

At Home: Have your child write a letter to a friend using two of the words from the box.

Name _____

As you read <u>Kate's Game</u>, fill in the Predictions Chart.

What I Predict	What Happens

How does the Predictions Chart help you understand
what happens in <u>Kate's Game</u>?

At Home: Have your child use the chart to retell the story.

© Macmillan/McGraw-Hill

Name _____

A **prediction** is a guess about what will happen next.

There is pizza on a plate. A good **prediction** would be that someone will eat the pizza.

Draw a line connecting each sentence with the one that tells what will happen next.

1. The block falls down.   Tim will pick it up.

2. The frog sees a pond.   The vet will help.

3. A dog is sick.   It will hop in.

4. Dad gets a cake.   She will run fast.

5. Jan gets a doll.   She will play with it.

6. Peg is late for school.   He eats it.

Make your own prediction.

7. Jake has a gift from his friend Meg.

_____

- -

_____

At Home: Look at the cover and title of a book. Ask your child to predict what the story might be about.

Name _____

Look at the word: **wave**

Notice that the **e** is dropped when adding **-ing** or **-ed**.

wav**e** + **ing** = wav**ing**   wav**e** + **ed** = wav**ed**

Add -ing to the words. Write the new word.

1. fake _____

2. rake _____

Add -ed to the words. Write the new word.

3. bake _____

4. fade _____

5. wade _____

At Home: With your child, read the new words and make sentences using the words.

Kate's Game • **Book 1.3/Unit 3**   89

Name _____

As I read, I will pay attention to the punctuation.

	You could help a friend pull a wagon.
8	You could pull a sled.
13	You could wave "Hello" to a friend.
20	You could make a card for a friend and write
30	"Hello."
31	Could you be a friend? Oh, yes! Oh, yes!
40	Look at all the ways to be a good friend! 50

Comprehension Check

1. How can you be a friend?

2. How do you help your friends?

	Words Read	–	Number of Errors	=	Words Correct Score
First Read		–		=	
Second Read		–		=	

At Home: Help your child read the passage, paying attention to the goal at the top of the page.

A **map** can show where streets are. Some maps have **labels** that tell where places are.

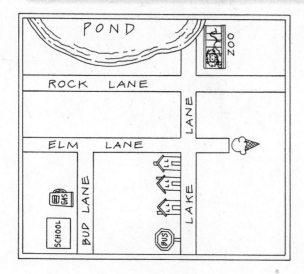

Look at the street map. Write the answers to the questions.

1. Where is the school? _____
   _____

2. What is next to the pond? _____
   _____

3. Where is the bus stop? _____
   _____

4. What lane stops at the pond? _____

5. How many houses are on Lake Lane?
   _____
   _____

At Home: With your child, draw a map of your neighborhood. Label the places on the map.

Name _____

Circle the word that completes each sentence.
Write the word on the line.

1. I can make a _____.

               cap   cake

2. Did you _____ Jen?

           tap   tape

3. Play a _____ with me.

        gap   game

4. I hit the ball with a _____.

           bat   bake

5. Shut the _____.

          gab   gate

6. We will jump in the _____.

          last   lake

7. Is the dog for _____?

          sap   sale

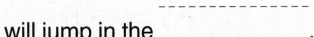

© Macmillan/McGraw-Hill

At Home: Have your child write the long *a* words and underline the *a* and *e* in each word. Talk about the pattern.

Name _____

Sometimes two consonants form a **blend**. You can hear each consonant sound in a **consonant blend**. Listen for the blend at the beginning of the word. **sl**ed

Use these blends to complete the words.

| sn | st | sm | sc | sp | sw |

1. _____amp

2. _____ap

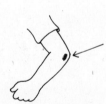

3. _____ab

4. _____ock

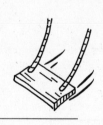

5. _____ing

6. _____in

At Home: Take turns with your child choosing a word from the page and using it in a sentence.

When	water	care	together
boy	people	girl	

Use the words from the box to complete the sentences.

1. The ⬚⬚⬚ can help.

2. The ⬚⬚⬚ can pick up.

3. Some ⬚⬚⬚⬚ go to school.

4. I ⬚⬚⬚⬚ about my mom.

5. ⬚⬚⬚⬚ can we ride?

6. Tad jumps into the ⬚⬚⬚⬚.

7. Bess and Jan play ⬚⬚⬚⬚⬚⬚⬚.

At Home: Write the words *boy, girl* and *people* on cards. Look in magazines to find pictures to match each word.

Name _____

As you read <u>Kids Can Help</u>, fill in the Compare and Contrast Chart.

Job	Kids in One Place	Kids in Another Place

How does the Compare and Contrast Chart help you better understand <u>Kids Can Help</u>?

At Home: Have your child use the chart to retell the story.

© Macmillan/McGraw-Hill

When you **compare** two or more things, you tell how they are **alike.**

When you **contrast** two or more things, you tell how they are **different.**

Color the picture if the sentence tells how two or more things are alike.

1. Jan and Fred run fast.

2. Tom has a red cap. Bess has a black cap.

3. One cat is little. One cat is big.

4. Sid and Sal play ball.

5. All the kids go to school.

6. Both girls like to play.

© Macmillan/McGraw-Hill

At Home: Have your child compare and contrast two shoes. Talk about the similarities and the differences.

Name _____

A **syllable** is a part of a word.

You can count the number of syllables in a word by counting the number of beats in the word.

Read the words below. Listen to the number of syllables in each word.

spud = 1   pump•kin = 2

Read each word. Circle the number of syllables in each word.

1. snack

1   2

2. stop

1   2

3. basket

1   2

4. swim

1   2

5. spin

1   2

6. wagon

1   2

7. under

1   2

8. spill

1   2

At Home: Have a home-based scavenger hunt for items with two syllables (e.g., scissors, carpet).

As I read, I will pay attention to punctuation.

	People all over like holidays. People come
7	together to do things on holidays. People
14	have holiday fun!
17	Today people give thanks for the things they
25	have. They have lots of good things to eat.
34	Today boys and girls are together at a
42	parade. It is fun when the big dragon comes
51	along. 52

Comprehension Check

1. Why do people like holidays?

2. What did the boys and girls see at the parade?

	Words Read	–	Number of Errors	=	Words Correct Score
First Read		–		=	
Second Read		–		=	

At Home: Help your child read the passage, paying attention to the goal at the top of the page.

Writers use interesting and colorful words.
The **fluffy, white** clouds float in the sky.

Circle the two words that a writer could use to describe each picture.

1. fast   soft   red

2. many   little   wet

3. black   one   hot

4. three   big   hot

5. little   many   big

6. hot   stink   yum

© Macmillan/McGraw-Hill

At Home: Together, read a poem. Listen for all the colorful
and interesting words the writer uses.

Name _____

Write the correct word in each sentence.

1. Beth slept in a _____.   tent
    stop

2. A _____ is in the box.   sniff
    snake

3. Do not _____ on the spill!   slip
    sled

4. I like to _____ at the park.   swing
    swat

5. A _____ is under the log.   slim
    slug

6. Look out for the _____!   skunk
    skin

7. Mom made a _____.   stem
    list

8. Put on a _____.   smock
    smell

At Home: Look at all the blends on the page. Help your child to notice that blends may be at the beginning or end of a word.

Practice

Name _____

Digraphs:
ch, wh, tch

The letters **ch** and **tch** stand for the sound you hear in **ch**op and fe**tch**.

The letters **wh** stand for the sound you hear in **wh**ale.

Circle the word that describes each picture. Then write the word on the line.

1.

watch   itch   catch

_____

2.

where   when   whale

_____

3.

inch   lunch   chunk

_____

4.

patch   switch   match

_____

 At Home: Help your child to use one of the circled words to write a sentence about day or night.

Name _____

Write words from the box to complete the story.

Your	light	our	again	Would

_____

1. _____ you like to play today?

2. The sun is up and it is _____ out.

3. We can ride _____ bikes.

4. _____ dog can run with us.

5. He is fast! Let's race _____.

At Home: Encourage your child to tell you about a favorite thing to do on a sunny day.

Name _____

**As you read <u>Short Shadows, Long Shadows</u>,
fill in the Main Idea and Details Web.**

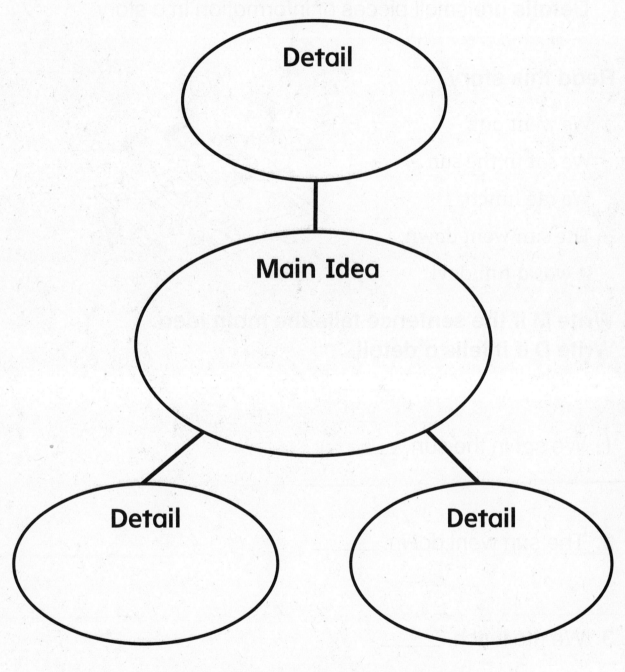

Detail

Main Idea

Detail

Detail

How does the Main Idea and Details Web help you
better understand the main idea of <u>Short Shadows,
Long Shadows</u>?

At Home: Have your child use the chart to retell the story.

Short Shadows, Long Shadows
Book 1.3/Unit 3

103

The **Main Idea** is the most important idea in the story.
Details are small pieces of information in a story.

Read this story.

We went out.

We sat in the sun.

We ate lunch.

The sun went down.

It was a fun day!

Write <u>M</u> if the sentence tells the main idea.
Write <u>D</u> if it tells a detail.

_____

------

1. We sat in the sun. _____

_____

------

2. The sun went down. _____

_____

------

3. We ate lunch. _____

_____

------

4. It was a fun day! _____

At Home: Help your child to think of more
details to put in the story.

Name _____

You can add **-s** or **-es** to name more than one person or thing.

Circle the word in each group that names more than one. Write it on the line.

1. watch   watches   what   _____

2. inches   pitch   inch   _____

3. such   lunch   lunches   _____

4. catch   patches   patch   _____

5. kisses   miss   kiss   _____

6. less   dresses   dress   _____

At Home: Have your child write a sentence using one of the -es words on the page.

As I read, I will pay attention to the questions.

	What makes a shadow?
4	Sun makes light and light makes a shadow.
12	When the sun is out you can see your
21	shadow. We would not see our shadows if
29	the sun was not out.
34	This groundhog is coming out of its den.
42	The groundhog will see its shadow if the sun
51	is out. 53

Comprehension Check

1. What makes a shadow?

2. When will a groundhog see its shadow?

	Words Read	−	Number of Errors	=	Words Correct Score
First Read		−		=	
Second Read		−		=	

At Home: Help your child read the passage, paying attention to the goal at the top of the page.

Name _____

The **title** of a magazine is on the **cover.**
There are **articles** inside the magazine.

Use the <u>magazine cover</u> and <u>article</u> to answer the questions.

1. What is the title of the magazine?

_____

- -

_____

2. What is on the cover?

_____

- -

_____

3. What is the title of the article?

_____

- -

_____

4. What could the article be about?

_____

- -

_____

At Home: Help your child to recognize titles and articles in a
magazine you read at home.

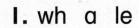
Blend the sounds to say each word. Write the word. Circle the picture it describes.

1. wh a le

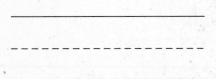

_____

- - - - - - - - - - - -

_____

2. h a tch

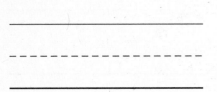

_____

- - - - - - - - - - - -

_____

3. ch e ck

_____

- - - - - - - - - - - -

_____

4. i tch

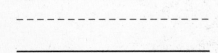

_____

- - - - - - - - - - - -

_____

   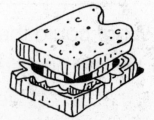

At Home: Have your child write and then illustrate a sentence using one of the words on the page.

Use the words in the box to complete the sentences.

hike	hive	line	bite	bike

1. Matt races very fast on his _____.

2. What will I find in the _____?

3. We must all walk in a _____.

4. Dan takes a big _____ of his cake.

5. We can _____ up this hill.

At Home: Help your child to make up a sentence for each word in the box.

Smile, Mike! • Book 1.3/Unit 3   109

Name _____

Use the words from the box to complete the story.

call	How	more	funny	There	so

Look! _____ is a pet show today.

I will _____ my dog Max.

_____ many pets will be in the show today?

Will they like Max _____ than the other pets in line?

We like to watch some of the _____ dogs and cats.

My Max is _____ good!

At Home: Have your child use some of the words from the box to tell another story about Max.

As you read Smile, Mike!, fill in the Predictions Chart.

What I Predict	What Happens

How does the Predictions Chart help you understand what happens in Smile, Mike!?

 At Home: Have your child use the chart to retell the story.

Smile, Mike! • **Book 1.3/Unit 3** 111

Read the sentences. Write the words that tell what happens next.

1. Tim's kite is ripped. Dad can fix Tim's kite.

_____

Tim will _____.

2. Kim must wash her dog. Kim's dog is very big.

_____

Mike will _____.

3. Sam wants to skate. Dad takes Sam to the rink.

_____

Sam and Dad will _____.

4. Sam wants a nice pup. Mom and Sam go to see the pups.

_____

Mom and Sam will _____.

© Macmillan/McGraw-Hill

At Home: Have your child talk about what will happen next in one of the stories.

When you add **–ed** or **–ing** to a word that ends with a vowel and a consonant, double the final consonant.

run + ing = ru**nn**ing   My dog is **running** fast.

chop + ed = cho**pp**ed   Sam **chopped** the log.

Read the sentence. Write the correct form of the word in the sentence.

1. Mike is _____ the ball with a bat.
       hit

2. The girl _____ the nice red mug.
        chip

3. The kids are _____ the parts
           put
of the kite together.

4. My dog just _____ over his dish.
          tip

At Home: Have your child write a sentence and draw a picture for one of the underlined words.

Smile, Mike! • Book 1.3/Unit 3   113

As I read, I will pay attention to the dialogue.

12	I did not want to play with Sam. So, I went to see Mom and Dad.
16	"Mom," I said. "How can I play? Sam will
25	not stop. He does just what I do."
33	"He's just a little boy," Mom said.
40	"He's just little," Dad said.
45	I said, "So can he play with you?"
53	"He can," they said. 57

Comprehension Check

1. What does Sam like to do?

2. How do Mom and Dad try to help?

	Words Read	–	Number of Errors	=	Words Correct Score
First Read		–		=	
Second Read		–		=	

At Home: Help your child read the passage, paying attention to the goal at the top of the page.

Read the chart.

Tim's Pets	Nan's Pets
cats |||	cat	
mice THL	mice ||
dog		dogs ||
fish THL ||||	fish THL THL

Count the pets and then complete the sentences.

_____

- - - - - - - - - - - - - -

1. Tim has _____ fish.

_____

- - - - - - - - - - - - - -

2. Nan has _____ mice.

_____

- - - - - - - - - - - - - -

3. Tim has _____ dog.

_____

- - - - - - - - - - - - - -

4. Nan has _____ fish.

At Home: Together, decide which child, Tim or Nan, has more pets.

Smile, Mike! • **Book 1.3/Unit 3**   115

© Macmillan/McGraw-Hill

Name _____

Use the words in the box to answer the riddles.

bike	hit	slide	slip	dig

1. You do this on the ice. What word am I?

_____

- - - - - - - - - - - -

_____

2. You ride me fast up a hill. What word am I?

_____

- - - - - - - - - - - -

_____

3. You do this in the sand. What word am I?

_____

- - - - - - - - - - - -

_____

4. You do this with a bat in a game. What word am I?

_____

- - - - - - - - - - - -

_____

5. You like to race down me. What word am I?

_____

- - - - - - - - - - - -

_____

© Macmillan/McGraw-Hill

At Home: Together, use some of the words in the box to make up a story. Then ask your child to illustrate it.

Name _____

Three letters can form a **blend**.
Listen for all three consonant sounds in each blend.

spring

scratch

splash

Write the new word on the line.
Connect the word to the matching picture.

_____

- - - - - - - - - - - - - - - - - - -

1. scr + atch = _____

_____

- - - - - - - - - - - - - - - - - - -

2. str + ipe = _____

_____

- - - - - - - - - - - - - - - - - - -

3. spr + ing = _____

_____

- - - - - - - - - - - - - - - - - - -

4. spl + it = _____

© Macmillan/McGraw-Hill

At Home: Have your child add *str-* to each word ending: *ap,*
-ing, -etch, and *-ip.* Together, read the new words.

| say | says | about | give | read | were |

Use the words from the box to complete the sentences.

1. Here is a book _____ cats.

2. "What is it?" _____ Gram.

3. "Will you _____ it?" I ask.

4. I _____ her the book.

5. "It's a good book," we _____ together.

6. We _____ glad we could read it.

© Macmillan/McGraw-Hill

At Home: Have your child think of different sentences for the words in the box.

As you read <u>Gram and Me</u>, fill in the Character and Setting Chart.

Setting	What the Characters Do There
1.	1.
2.	2.
3.	3.
4.	4.

How does the Character and Setting Chart help you retell <u>Gram and Me</u>?

 At Home: Have your child use the chart to retell the story.

The **setting** is where a story takes place.

The **characters** are the people or animals in a story.

setting

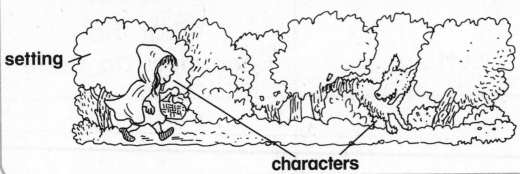

characters

Think about what a school setting is like. Circle the people and things you would find in a school.

desk

bike

girl

book

pen

skate

animal

boy

© Macmillan/McGraw-Hill

At Home: Help your child list the people and things he or she would see in your home.

Name _____

Contractions combine two words. The **apostrophe** (')
takes the place of any missing letters.

we + will = **we'll**   I + am = **I'm**   you + have = **you've**

Write the contraction for the two words.

1. we + have = _____

2. he + will = _____

3. I + am = _____

4. she + will = _____

Use the contractions to complete the sentences.

5. _____ itching my scratch.

6. _____ be glad when spring is here.

© Macmillan/McGraw-Hill

At Home: Write sentences describing things your family will
do this week. Begin each sentence with *"We'll."*

Gram and Me • **Book 1.3/Unit 3**   121

As I read, I will pay attention to the dialogue.

	"Hi, Grandpa!" I say.
4	I give my Grandpa a big hug.
11	"I'm looking at pictures," says Grandpa.
17	"Would you like me to tell you about them?"
26	"This is me when I was little," says Grandpa.
35	"I liked to write stories on that typewriter."
43	"I like to write stories, too," I say. "I write
53	them on my computer." 57

Comprehension Check

1. What are Grandpa and the boy doing?

2. How are Grandpa and the boy alike?

	Words Read	–	Number of Errors	=	Words Correct Score
First Read		–		=	
Second Read		–		=	

At Home: Help your child read the passage, paying attention to the goal at the top of the page.

Name _____

A **numerical list** is a series of things written in
1, 2, 3 order.

Make two lists. Use the words below to help you.

pen	pants	tape
hat	desk	socks

Things for a Trip **Things for School**

1. _____

2. _____

3. _____

1. _____

2. _____

3. _____

**Draw a picture of something else you need at
school.**

At Home: Help your child make a list of things to take
on a picnic.

Gram and Me • Book 1.3/Unit 3   123

Write the word that completes each sentence.

_____

- - - - - - - - - - - - - - - - - -

1. I can _____ the plum.

      string   smell   shade

_____

- - - - - - - - - - - - - - - - - - - -

2. I would like a _____.

      snack   scratch   snap

_____

- - - - - - - - - - - - - - - - - - - -

3. The _____ cat likes to play with string.

      striped   scarf   steps

_____

- - - - - - - - - - - - - - - - - - - -

4. Boys and girls like to _____ in the water.

      split   splash   scat

_____

- - - - - - - - - - - - - - - - - - - -

5. The _____ is hot!

      sleet   strip   stove

_____

- - - - - - - - - - - - - - - - - - - -

6. Many people like the _____.

      snap   split   spring

At Home: Help your child circle any blends he or she sees in the words on this page.

Write the word that completes each sentence.

Would	read	How	together	funny

_____
- -

1. They ride _____.

_____
- -

2. _____ much is that?

_____
- -

3. They have _____ hats.

_____
- -

4. The boys like to _____.

_____
- -

5. _____ you like to bat?

Name _____

Write the word that completes each sentence.

_____

- - - - - - - - - - - - - - - - - - - -

I. _____ you help us?

       Could   Care

_____

- - - - - - - - - - - - - - - - - - - -

2. Three _____ are eating lunch.

       people   walk

_____

- - - - - - - - - - - - - - - - - - - -

3. She will take _____ of the fish.

       there   care

_____

- - - - - - - - - - - - - - - - - - - -

4. _____ mom will pick you up.

       Your   Were

_____

- - - - - - - - - - - - - - - - - - - -

5. I would like to play _____.

       oh   again

_____

- - - - - - - - - - - - - - - - - - - -

6. The light _____ we can walk.

       says   give

© Macmillan/McGraw-Hill

Name _____

Use the words in the box to complete the sentences.

rode	close	joke	bone
hope	drove	rose	

1. The pet shop is _____ to my home.

2. The _____ is red and smells nice.

3. My dad _____ us home after the game.

4. We _____ on the bus to get to school.

5. I broke the _____ in my leg when I fell.

6. I _____ I win a big prize!

7. Can you tell a funny _____?

At Home: Have your child write a sentence for another long *o* word.

Use the words from the box to complete the sentences.

opened	every	any	saw
soon	sparkled	floating	

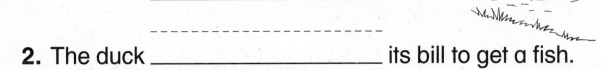

1. I _____ a big, fat duck.

2. The duck _____ its bill to get a fish.

3. The duck was _____ on the pond.

4. The pond's water _____ in the sun.

5. I did not see _____ other ducks.

6. _____ the duck swam away.

7. I go to the pond _____ day.

At Home: Help your child to write a fun sentence using a word from the box.

© Macmillan/McGraw-Hill

Name _____

As you read Pelican Was Hungry, fill in the Inference Chart.

Text Clues	What You Know	Inferences

How does the Inference Chart help you better understand Pelican Was Hungry?

At Home: Have your child use the chart to retell the story.

Pelican Was Hungry
Book 1.4/Unit 4

129

© Macmillan/McGraw-Hill

Name _____

**Use the picture and what you already know
about birds to decide if the sentences are true.
Write T if the sentence is true.
Write F if the sentence is false.**

1. The bird lives in a tree with its babies. _____

2. The big bird can fly. _____

3. The bird is as big as a pelican. _____

4. The nest is made of stones. _____

5. The big bird is the mother. _____

6. The little birds like to eat only fish. _____

7. Soon the little birds will fly, too. _____

At Home: Talk with your child about three facts he or she
has learned about birds.

As I read, I will pay attention to the punctuation.

	Penguins can dive. They dive under the water
8	to get food. Penguins eat fish. They eat krill
17	that are small shrimp.
21	Every year, penguins make nests on the land.
29	Some penguins use stones to make a nest.
37	Some penguins make a hole.
42	They fill it with grass to make a nest.
51	This penguin has an egg.
56	The penguin will keep the egg warm. 63

Comprehension Check

1. What do penguins eat?

2. How do penguins make nests?

	Words Read	–	Number of Errors	=	Words Correct Score
First Read		–		=	
Second Read		–		=	

At Home: Help your child read the passage, paying attention to the goal at the top of the page.

A **dictionary** is a book that gives the meaning of words. Some words have more than one meaning.

Read the definitions below.

bark 1. the outside cover of a tree: The **bark** on the tree fell off. **2.** to make the sound that a dog makes: His dog will **bark** at all cats.

seal 1. an animal that lives in the ocean most of the time and swims very well: The **seal** swam over the wave. **2.** to close something so that it can not be opened: I had to **seal** the box with tape to close it.

Choose the correct definition for the word.
Fill in the circle.

1. bark   ○ drop a pole   ○ be like a dog

2. bark   ○ on a tree   ○ in a pot

3. seal   ○ run away   ○ close a box very well

4. seal   ○ a blue ship   ○ an animal that swims

Use a word from above in a sentence.

_____

_ _

_____

At Home: Make up a silly sentence using the two meanings of the word *bark*.

Name _____

Circle the word that completes each sentence.
Then write the word.

_____
- - - - - - - - - - - - - - - - - - - -

I. A dog can run _____ than a cat.

faster   fastest

_____
- - - - - - - - - - - - - - - - - - - -

2. A cat can run _____ than a duck.

faster   fastest

_____
- - - - - - - - - - - - - - - - - - - -

3. The dog is the _____ of them all.

faster   fastest

_____
- - - - - - - - - - - - - - - - - - - -

4. That little bed is _____ than my bed.

softer   softest

_____
- - - - - - - - - - - - - - - - - - - -

5. The big bed is the _____ of them all.

softer   softest

At Home: Ask your child to use *faster* and *fastest* in two
sentences that compare people or animals.

Pelican Was Hungry   **133**
Book 1.4/Unit 4

© Macmillan/McGraw-Hill

Poems often repeat words or sentences more than once.

Read the poem. Then answer the questions.

The Pelican and the Fish

The fish swims.
The pelican flies over.
The fish swims.
The pelican is hungry.
The fish swims.
The pelican dives down.
The fish swims.

_____

- -

The pelican _____

GULP!

1. Circle the sentences that repeat.

2. Complete the end of the poem.

At Home: Help your child to read the poem aloud with
expression.

Name _____

Circle the word that names each picture. Then write the word.

1.

bake   bike

_____

- - - - - - - - - - - - - -

2.

shape   ship

_____

- - - - - - - - - - - - - -

3.

skates   stones

_____

- - - - - - - - - - - - - -

4.

grabs   grapes

_____

- - - - - - - - - - - - - -

5.

strip   stripe

_____

- - - - - - - - - - - - - -

6. **9**

nose   nine

_____

- - - - - - - - - - - - - -

7.

snack   snake

_____

- - - - - - - - - - - - - -

8.

smoke   smile

_____

- - - - - - - - - - - - - -

At Home: Have your child think of one more long *o*, long *i*, and long *a* word.

The letters **u** and **e** stand for the **long u** sound.

cub**e**   tun**e**

Use words from the box to complete each sentence.

June   tube   dune   Luke   flute   mule

_____
- - - - - - - - - - - - - - - - - - - -

1. What is inside this _____?

_____
- - - - - - - - - - - - - - - - - - - -

2. We ran down the sand _____
and into the water.

_____
- - - - - - - - - - - - - - - - - - - -

3. The baby plays with his stuffed _____.

_____   _____
- - - - - - - - - - - -   - - - - - - - - - - - -

4. _____ and _____
are six.

_____
- - - - - - - - - - - - - - - - - - - -

5. I can play a tune on my _____.

At Home: Ask your child to use two of the long *u* words in a sentence.

Name _____

Write the word that completes each sentence.

| find | after | old | new | terrific |

1. Dad has _____ socks for

Kim because hers are _____.

2. Can you help me _____ my glasses?

3. We go to the park _____ school.

We have a _____ time.

Match the word to its meaning.

4. done   something you make or invent

5. work   finished

6. creation   to do a job

 At Home: Ask your child to use two words from the box in sentences.

As you read <u>June Robot Cleans Up</u>, fill in the Conclusion Chart.

Inference	Inference

Conclusion

· ·

Inference	Inference

Conclusion

How does the Conclusion Chart help you better understand <u>June Robot Cleans Up</u>?

© Macmillan/McGraw-Hill

At Home: Have your child use the chart to retell the story.

> You can use what you read and what you already know to help you **draw conclusions.**

Read each story. Draw a conclusion about the characters. Then fill in the circle of the sentence that makes the most sense with the story.

1. Jane bikes to school. She likes to run races. She has fun jumping rope. Jane plays ball with her pals, too.

   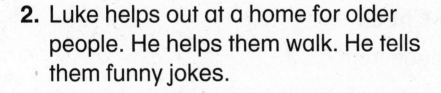

   ○ Jane is in good shape.

   ○ Jane likes to take care of dogs.

2. Luke helps out at a home for older people. He helps them walk. He tells them funny jokes.

   ○ Luke is like the older people.

   ○ Luke likes to help older people.

© Macmillan/McGraw-Hill

At Home: Ask your child to draw another conclusion about Jane and Luke.

June Robot Cleans Up
Book 1.4/Unit 4
139

As I read, I will pay attention to the punctuation.

	Paper is made from trees. It takes many,
8	many trees to make the paper people use.
16	How can people help to save trees?
23	In some places, workers collect paper for
30	recycling. Recycling is making new things
36	from old things. Sometimes people bring
42	paper to a recycling center.
47	Old paper is recycled into new paper at a
56	mill. Look and see how it is done. 64

Comprehension Check

1. What is paper made from?

2. How can people help to save trees?

	Words Read	–	Number of Errors	=	Words Correct Score
First Read		–		=	
Second Read		–		=	

June Robot Cleans Up
Book 1.4/Unit 4

At Home: Help your child read the passage, paying attention to the goal at the top of the page.

Context clues are words in a sentence that help you figure out the meaning of a new word.

Use context clues to figure out the meaning of the underlined word. Fill in the circle next to the correct answer.

1. Plants need water and sunlight to grow and stay <u>alive</u>.

   ○ living

   ○ outside

2. Mom picked a <u>bunch</u> of roses from the garden.

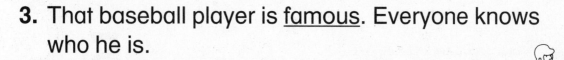

   ○ something that is red

   ○ a group of things

3. That baseball player is <u>famous</u>. Everyone knows who he is.

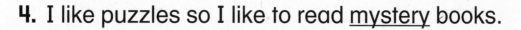

   ○ very well known

   ○ sad

4. I like puzzles so I like to read <u>mystery</u> books.

   ○ a story, play, or movie that has a puzzle to solve

   ○ a story that is very funny

The Case of the Missing Ring

At Home: Write a sentence using one of the underlined words.

Read the **CVCe** words. Listen for the long vowel sound.

cu**be**   la**ce**   ri**de**

Circle the word that names the picture. Then write the word.

1. game   gate   _____

2. bate   bone   _____

3. flute   flat   _____

4. fine   five   _____

5. cub   cube   _____

Read your answers. Then complete this sentence.

6. Words with CVCe have a _____ vowel sound.

At Home: Help your child to find CVCe words in a favorite book.

Name _____

A **floor plan** is a drawing that shows where things are in a room.

Use the floor plan to complete each sentence.

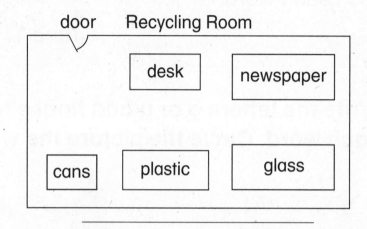

door   Recycling Room

desk   newspaper

cans   plastic   glass

_____

- - - - - - - - - - - - - - - - - - - -

1. The cans bin is next to the _____ bin.

2. If you can't tell which bin something goes in,

_____

- - - - - - - - - - - - - - - - - - - -

ask for help at the _____.

_____

- - - - - - - - - - - - - - - - - - - -

3. Put  in the _____ bin.

_____

- - - - - - - - - - - - - - - - - - - -

4. These ![newspaper] go in the _____ bin.

_____

- - - - - - - - - - - - - - - - - - - -

5. The smallest bin is for _____.

At Home: Have your child draw a floor plan of his or her room. Help your child label the floor plan.

Name _____

Read the words.

Listen to the long vowel sound in each word.

June   Rose

Write the letters <u>o</u> or <u>u</u> and final <u>e</u> to complete each word. Circle the picture the word names.

1. c ___ b ___

2. b ___ n ___

 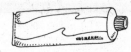

3. n ___ s ___

4. m ___ l ___

 **At Home:** Have your child find long *o* and long *u* words on store signs in your neighborhood.

Name _____

The letters **ay** and **ai** stand for the **long a** sound.

Jay
clay

Gail
sail

Use a word from the box to complete each sentence.

snail	pay	paint	clay

Ray

_____

- - - - - - - - - - - - - - - - - -

1. Ray will use some _____.

_____

- - - - - - - - - - - - - - -

2. He will _____ the vase gray.

_____

- - - - - - - - - - - - - - - - - -

3. She will _____ for the tray.

_____

- - - - - - - - - - - - - - - -

4. A _____ is on the pail.

At Home: Help your child to make up sentences with two long *a* words.

Name _____

Use words in the box to complete the sentences.

| Their | know | cold | warm | great |

1. I _____ how to ride a bike.

2. A hat helps keep you _____ in the winter.

3. Ice is very _____.

4. We had a _____ time at the party.

5. _____ dog is black and white.

Match the word to its meaning.

6. sound   very great; dangerous

7. predict   something you hear

8. extreme   to guess what will happen next

At Home: Ask your child to use two words from the box to make up original sentences.

Name _____

As you read Stormy Weather, fill in the Compare and Contrast Chart.

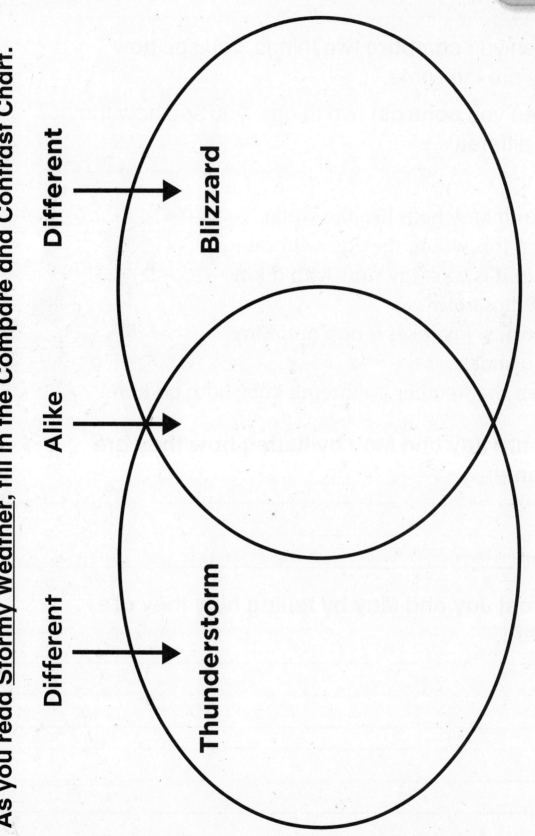

Different

Blizzard

Alike

Different

Thunderstorm

How does the Compare and Contrast Chart help you better understand Stormy Weather?

 At Home: Have your child use the chart to retell the story.

Name _____

When you **compare** two things, you see how they are the same.

When you **contrast** two things, you see how they are different.

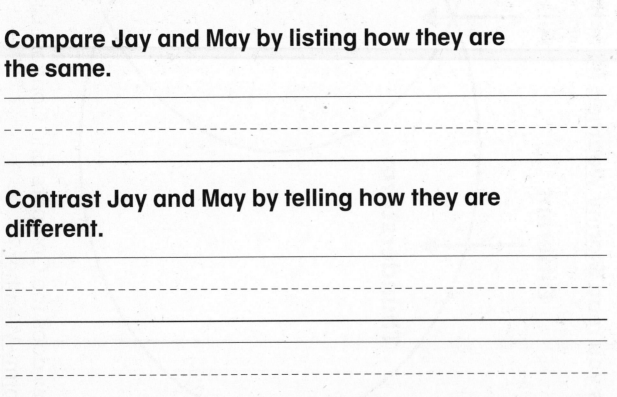

Jay and May both like the water.
When it is warm, they go swimming.
When it is cool, Jay runs with a kite.
May digs holes.
If it rains, Jay takes a nap and May has a snack.
When the weather is extreme, they both go home.

Compare Jay and May by listing how they are the same.

_____

- -

_____

Contrast Jay and May by telling how they are different.

_____

- -

_____

- -

_____

At Home: Ask your child to describe two friends. Have your child tell how they are alike and how they are different.

Read the definitions.

> **block** 1. An area between two streets: Sam lives on my **block**. 2. Something hard with flat sides: Put the toy **block** on top.
>
> **light** 1. Not heavy: The empty bag was **light**. 2. Energy from the sun: The sun's **light** was very hot.

Fill in the circle of the meaning of each bolded word.

1. We live on the same **block**.

   ○ an area between two streets

   ○ something hard with flat sides

2. The **light** from the sun is bright.

   ○ not heavy

   ○ energy from the sun

3. My backpack is **light** when I have no books.

   ○ not heavy

   ○ energy from the sun

4. The baby played with a **block**.

   ○ an area between two streets

   ○ something hard with flat sides

At Home: Have your child think of another word that has multiple meanings.

As I read, I will pay attention to the punctuation.

	It is Sunday. People on TV predict the
8	weather. They let you know Sunday will be a
17	hot, sunny day.
20	Now you know what the weather will be. It's
29	a great day for swimming in the cold water!
38	It is Monday now. It is warm, but not sunny.
48	There are gray clouds everywhere. It may
55	rain.
56	It is Tuesday now. It is a rainy, wet day.
66	People will have to use their umbrellas. 73

Comprehension Check

1. What can you do on a hot, sunny day?

2. What would you use on a rainy day?

	Words Read	–	Number of Errors	=	Words Correct Score
First Read		–		=	
Second Read		–		=	

© Macmillan/McGraw-Hill

At Home: Help your child read the passage, paying attention to the goal at the top of the page.

Name _____

A **telephone directory** lists names, addresses, and telephone numbers.

Vann,	Jay	17 Elm Ave.	555-5436
Vann,	Max	17 Elm Ave.	555-5436
Wade,	Jake	245 Main St.	555-7401
Wade,	Lon	29 Sunset Ave.	555-4269
Wade,	May	9 Sunrise St.	555-9711

Use the directory to complete each question.

1. How many people have the last name Wade? _____

2. What is May Wade's phone number? _____

3. Where does Jake Wade live? _____

4. Who has the same address and telephone number?

_____

_____

At Home: Ask your child other questions using the information on the telephone directory above.

Stormy Weather • Book 1.4/Unit 4   151

A **compound word** is made up
of two small words.

rose + bush = **rosebush**

back + yard = **backyard**

**Match a word on the left to a word on the right to
make a compound word. Then write the word.**

1. bath   hill   _____

2. down   one   _____

3. any   care   _____

4. day   robe   _____

Use a compound word in a sentence.

_____

5. _____

At Home: Ask your child to look for compound words in a
magazine or newspaper.

Name _____

Use the words from the box to name each picture.

| rose | globe | tune | mule | snail | hay |

1.

_____

_____

2.

_____

_____

3.

_____

_____

4.

_____

_____

5.

_____

_____

6.

_____

_____

At Home: Have your child think of other words with the
long *o,* the long *u,* and the long *a* sounds.

Name _____

Listen to the sound the letters **ee, ea,** and **e** stand for.

t**ee**th   s**ea**l    h**e**

Circle the word that names each picture. Then write the word.

1. sheet   she   _____

2. peel   peek   _____

3. bean   beak   _____

4. weak   wheat   _____

5. seat   seed   _____

6. eat   eel   _____

© Macmillan/McGraw-Hill

At Home: Help your child to write a sentence for each of the circled words.

Read each sentence. Choose the word that completes the sentence. Circle the word.

1. Dan plays with his _____.

   friends   house

2. They came _____ Dean's house.

   by   knew

3. This game is _____ of like tag.

   kind   by

4. Jean said she could _____ far.

   run   curious

5. "I _____ you were it!" she said.

   knew   kind

6. Mike likes to look. He is _____.

   friends   curious

7. Dean has another _____.

   idea   knew

8. "I'm so glad we went to Dean's _____," said Mike.

   friends   house

At Home: Have your child write another sentence using one of the circled words.

Name _____

As you read <u>Meet Ben Franklin</u>, fill in the Inference Chart.

Text Clues	What You Know	Inferences

How does the Inference Chart help you better understand <u>Meet Ben Franklin</u>?

At Home: Have your child use the chart to retell the story.

Read the story. Then choose an answer to complete each sentence.

Jean puts a cast on a cat. Then she looks at a man's dog. The dog's teeth are bad. "Please brush your dog's teeth," she tells the man. Today she takes care of many pets. "Oh, no!" says Jean. "I did not eat lunch yet."

1. Jean _____.

   ○ works in a lab

   ○ is a vet

   ○ likes to read

2. Why does Jean put a cast on the cat? _____

   ○ The cat goes to sleep.

   ○ The cat wants to eat.

   ○ The cat broke a leg.

3. Jean asks the man to brush his dog's teeth so that _____.

   ○ she will not have to pull any teeth

   ○ she can eat lunch

   ○ the dog can run faster

4. Jean did not eat lunch because she _____.

   ○ was not hungry

   ○ forgot

   ○ had no pets to take care of

At Home: Ask your child to explain how he or she figured out
the answer to each question.

As I read, I will pay attention to the punctuation.

How Far Down Did Sylvia Dive?

6	Sylvia did something that no one had done
14	before her. She went 1,250 feet down into
21	the ocean. That's far!
25	Sylvia walked on the sea floor. Like the
33	men who walked on the moon, she had an
42	American flag with her.
46	Going down 1,250 feet was amazing.
51	But Sylvia knew she wanted to go deeper.
59	An underwater sub like this one took Sylvia
67	down 3,000 feet! 69

Comprehension Check

1. What did Sylvia do that no one else had done before?

2. What country do you think Sylvia is from?

	Words Read	–	Number of Errors	=	Words Correct Score
First Read		–		=	
Second Read		–		=	

© Macmillan/McGraw-Hill

At Home: Help your child read the passage, paying attention to the goal at the top of the page.

A verb is a word that shows action.
You can add **–ed** or **–ing** to most verbs.
A verb with an **–ed** ending means the action
happened in the past.

play + **ing** = playing

play + **ed** = played

Write each verb with –ing and –ed.

1. flash _____ _____

2. pull _____ _____

3. fill _____ _____

Use an –ing word and -ed word in sentences.

4. _____

At Home: Think about the words *talk* and *listen*. Say each
word with the endings *–ed* and *–ing*.

Meet Ben Franklin
Book 1.4/Unit 4

159

These words follow the CVVC pattern:

b**oa**t   k**ee**p   s**ea**t   r**ai**n

Use <u>oa</u>, <u>ee</u>, <u>ea</u>, or <u>ai</u> to complete the name for each picture.

1. b_____t

2. s_____d

3. b_____k

4. w_____t

5. l_____f

6. g_____t

At Home: Have your child think of two more words with the CVVC pattern and draw a picture for each word.

© Macmillan/McGraw-Hill

Bold print points out important words.

Read the story. Then write the answer to each question below.

Ben Franklin was an **inventor**. He came up with ideas for many things that would help to make people's lives better. His **Franklin Stove** was a much safer way for people to burn wood for heat and for cooking. Even now we use a **lightning rod** to protect houses and ships from lightning. He gave his inventions away for **free**.

1. What is an inventor?

_____

- -

_____

2. What did people use as a safer way to burn wood?

_____

- -

_____

3. What does a lightning rod do?

_____

- -

_____

© Macmillan/McGraw-Hill

At Home: Together, look through one of your child's text books for words in bold print. Ask your child why the words are shown in bold print.

Meet Ben Franklin
Book 1.4/Unit 4   161

Name _____

Look at the picture. Read the two words. Then use the words to write a silly sentence.

1. seal   read

_____

- -

_____

2. jet   teeth

_____

- -

_____

3. pet   net

_____

- -

_____

4. hen   feet

_____

- -

_____

At Home: With your child, write a silly sentence using any two words from this page.

Sometimes the letter **y** stands for the long **e** sound.   happ**y**

Circle the word that answers the question. Then write the word.

1. What can you ride in? _____

    buggy   jelly

2. What can you spend? _____

    muddy   penny

3. What do you call a very small boy? _____

    pony   baby

4. What do you call a baby dog? _____

    daisy   puppy

5. What can you call a rabbit? _____

    bunny   easy

At Home: Have your child think of one more word that ends with the long *e* sound.

Little Rabbit • **Book 1.4/Unit 4**   163

Name _____

Write words from the box to complete the story.

told	before	falls	began
haste	glared	happen	heard

_____

1. I _____ a loud crash!

2. Did something bad _____?

3. I ran with _____ to see.

4. I _____ at my sister and then

_____ to scold her.

5. I _____ her not to jump on the bed.

6. She _____ every time.

7. I hugged her _____ I left.

At Home: Together, use some of the words from the box to write sentences about a pet animal.

Name _____

As you read <u>Little Rabbit</u>, fill in the Beginning, Middle, and End Chart.

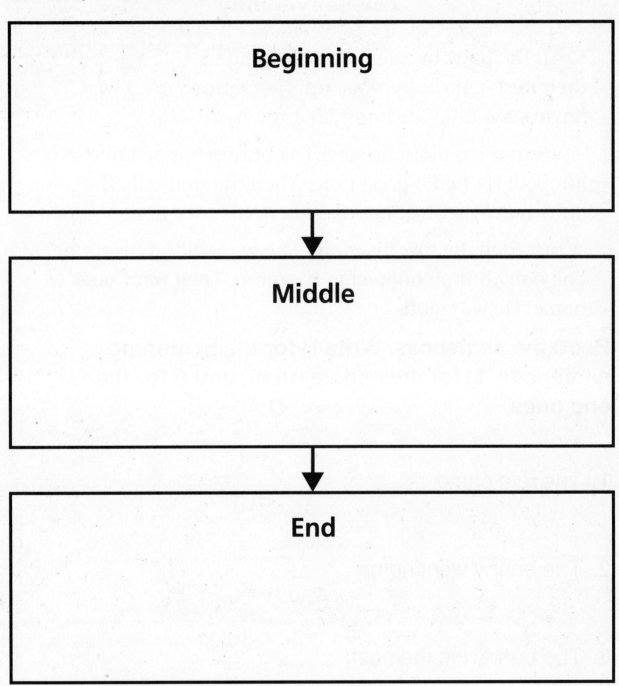

Beginning

Middle

End

How does the Beginning, Middle, and End Chart help you better understand <u>Little Rabbit</u>?

 At Home: Have your child use the chart to retell the story.

Read the story.

The Baby Bunny

All the baby bunnies were sleeping in their nest. One baby woke up. He planned to have some fun. The bunny left the nest.

What a big place he saw! The bunny hopped and jumped. He had a good time. Then the rain fell. The baby bunny wished he was safe in his cozy nest.

Just then, he saw his mom. She was calling his name. The baby bunny hopped to his mom. They went back home. He was glad.

Read the sentences. Write <u>B</u> for the beginning sentences, <u>M</u> for the middle ones, and <u>E</u> for the end ones.

1. The rain came. _____

2. The bunny went home. _____

3. The bunny left the nest. _____

4. The bunny had a good time. _____

 At Home: Ask your child to retell the story in the correct sequence and draw how the bunny looked when he got home.

As I read, I will pay attention to pauses, stops, and intonation in the passage.

	One day Lion closed his eyes. He wanted to
9	fall asleep. Then, Mouse came by. Lion heard
17	Mouse and woke up.
21	Lion stretched out his paw. He glared. Then he
30	grabbed the little mouse.
34	Mouse began to shake. He didn't want to fall.
43	"Great Lion, let me go!" said Mouse.
50	"Why should I let you go?" asked Lion.
58	Mouse said, "I am just a little mouse. But I can
69	be a good friend to you." 75

Comprehension Check

1. Why does Mouse shake?

2. Why does Mouse think Lion should let him go?

	Words Read	–	Number of Errors	=	Words Correct Score
First Read		–		=	
Second Read		–		=	

© Macmillan/McGraw-Hill

At Home: Help your child read the passage, paying attention to the goal at the top of the page.

> **Context clues** are words in a sentence that help
> you figure out the meaning of a new word.

**Use the underlined context clues to figure out the
meaning of the word in bold letters.**

1. The <u>apples</u> are **falling** <u>down</u> to the <u>ground</u>.

2. The <u>branches</u> and <u>leaves</u> <u>hide</u> <u>animals</u> in the **forest**.

3. I **heard** the <u>owl</u> <u>hoot</u>.

4. The <u>rabbit</u> <u>hopped</u> into the <u>bush</u> **before** the <u>fox</u> <u>saw it</u>.

Now match the word to its meaning:

1. falling   **a.** listened with ears

2. forest   **b.** to go from a high place to a low place

3. heard   **c.** at an earlier time

4. before   **d.** a place where trees and plants grow

© Macmillan/McGraw-Hill

At Home: Help your child to use context clues to figure out
unknown words on the page of a favorite book.

For words that end with a consonant followed by
y, change the **y** to **i** before adding **es.**

bun**ny**   bunn**ies**

**Read the word under each sentence. Change the
word by adding __es__. Then complete each sentence.**

_____

- -

1. The twin _____ smiled at me.
   baby

- -

2. Their _____ are full.
   tummy

- -

3. Jenny _____ math every day.
   study

- -

4. Tommy and Timmy are _____.
   buddy

- -

5. The _____ at the pet store were so cute.
   puppy

At Home: Read one of the words that end in -es. Have your
child say the base word and use it in a new sentence.

Little Rabbit • Book 1.4/Unit 4   169

Repetition is when some words or sentences in a story or poem are used again and again.

Read the story. Then underline the sentences that show repetition.

The Pond

One day a 🦁 came to the pond.

It drank some water.

Glug! Glug! Glug! Then it went off to rest.

A 🦓 came to the pond next.

It drank some water, too.

Glug! Glug! Glug! Then it went off to rest.

Then a big 🐘 came to the pond.

It drank, and it drank.

Glug! Glug! Glug! Then it went off to rest.

The 🦁 came back to the pond.

It wanted one more drink.

But there was no water left in the pond!

At Home: Together, sing songs with repeated lines, such as "Three Blind Mice." Talk about which lines are repeated in the song.

Name _____

Read the words. Then circle the words with the long <u>e</u> sound.

day	pay	buddy
happy	tummy	pony
say	daddy	play

Write a sentence. Use a word with the long <u>e</u> sound.

_____

- -

_____

Read the words. Then circle the words with the long <u>a</u> sound.

chilly	play	messy
tray	way	lucky
cozy	stay	gray

Write a sentence. Use a word with the long <u>a</u> sound.

_____

- -

_____

- -

_____

At Home: With your child, write the words from the boxes
and sort them into long *e* and long *a* words.

Name _____

Draw a line from the picture to the word that tells about it. Then write the word on the line.

warm

cold

extreme

1. _____

2. _____

knew

new

old

3. _____

4. _____

idea

creation

floating

5. _____

6. _____

Circle the word that goes in each sentence. Then write the word on the line.

_____

\- - - - - - - - - - - - - - - - - -

1. Mom rode the train to _____.

house   work

_____

\- - - - - - - - - - - - - - - - -

2. I read _____ I go to sleep.

before   after

_____

\- - - - - - - - - - - - - - - - - -

3. Use the hose _____ their house.

began   by

_____

\- - - - - - - - - - - - - - - - -

4. Do you know _____ cute jokes?

every   any

_____

\- - - - - - - - - - - - - - - - -

5. What _____ do you like?

find   kind

_____

\- - - - - - - - - - - - - - - - -

6. Have you _____ any great ideas?

heard   glared

There are different ways to make the **long o** sound. The letters **o**, **oa**, and **ow** stand for the **long o** sound.

g**o**   c**oa**t   cr**ow**

Circle the answer to each question.

1. What floats on water?
   a boat   a loaf

2. What can a bike do?
   so   go

3. What can you do to grass?
   flow   mow

4. What can a hose do?
   soak   roast

5. What do you sleep with?
   show   pillow

6. What can a tube do?
   float   goal

Use two long <u>o</u> words from above in sentences.

_____

7. _____

_____

8. _____

At Home: Listen to your child read the long *o* words and underline the letter or letters that stand for the long *o* sound.

© Macmillan/McGraw-Hill

mother	try	always	firm
father	love	supposed	

Use words from the box to complete the sentences.

1. My mom is my _____.

2. My dad is my _____.

3. We _____ each other.

4. We _____ help each other.

5. Mom and Dad _____ to be nice.

6. I am _____ to be good.

7. Sometimes they are _____ with me.

At Home: Choose three of the words. Then have your child write sentences for the words.

As you read <u>Olivia</u>, fill in the Fantasy and Reality Chart.

Reality	Fantasy
What Happens	**Why It Could Not Happen In Real Life**

How does the Fantasy and Reality Chart help you better understand <u>Olivia</u>?

At Home: Have your child use the chart to retell the story.

> **Reality** is something that could really happen.
>
> **Fantasy** is something that could not really happen.

Circle the sentences that show <u>reality</u>. Then underline the sentences that are <u>fantasy</u>.

1. A pig puts on a dress.

2. A pig paints.

3. A pig sleeps.

4. A pig goes to school.

5. A pig has a pet cat.

6. A pig sits in the mud.

7. A pig reads a book.

8. A pig has a mother.

© Macmillan/McGraw-Hill

At Home: Have your child write a story about a pig. Then talk about what is reality and what is fantasy in the story.

Olivia • **Book 1.5/Unit 5**   **177**

Name _____

As I read, I will pay attention to pauses for punctuation.

	Mike's class was at the art gallery.
7	"Always stay together, class," said Mrs. West.
14	"We don't want anyone to get lost."
21	The children stopped in one room. There were
29	many paintings to see.
33	"Come look at this one, Zack," said Mike.
41	Mike looked at the painting. There were people
49	rowing boats on a lake. Mike saw that one boat
59	had no one in it.
64	"I wish I could be in that boat," Mike said.
74	The next thing Mike knew, he was in the boat!
84	Mike put the oars in the water and pulled.
93	Just then Mike heard Zack say,
99	"Come on Mike. let's go."
104	"Wait until I tell you what happened," said Mike. 113

Comprehension Check

1. Where did Mike and his class go?

2. What happened to Mike at the art gallery?

	Words Read	–	Number of Errors	=	Words Correct Score
First Read		–		=	
Second Read		–		=	

© Macmillan/McGraw-Hill

At Home: Help your child read the passage, paying attention to the goal at the top of the page.

Name _____

Read the dictionary entries below.

> **middle** halfway between two ends: We stood in the **middle** of the line.
>
> **mistake** something thought or done incorrectly: I made one **mistake** on the spelling test.
>
> **protects** to keep away from harm: The mother hen protects her eggs.

Use a word from the box to complete each sentence. You may use a word more than once.

1. Joan sat in the _____ of her two friends.

2. The mother cat _____ her babies.

3. Please draw a line down the _____ of the paper.

4. If you make a _____, try again.

I want the yellow paint.

yellow red blue green

At Home: As you read together, find two words your child doesn't know. Work together to find the meanings of these words in the dictionary.

Adding the letter **y** to the end of some words makes a new word. Notice that **y** stands for the long **e** sound.

snow + **y** = snow**y**

Circle the correct word. Then write it on the line.

_____   soapy

1. The washcloth is _____.   soap

_____   toast

2. The campfire is _____.   toasty

_____   waxy

3. The apple feels _____.   wax

_____   fussy

4. The baby is _____ today.   fuss

_____   trick

5. The jigsaw puzzle is _____.   tricky

At Home: Have your child circle all the *y* endings.
Discuss what the base words are.

© Macmillan/McGraw-Hill

Name _____

> **Captions** tell readers more about a photograph or picture.

Circle the caption that tells about the picture.

1. a snake
a baby deer

2. Big Bass Lake
the waterslide

3. my new bike
Big Buck Forest

4. the swimming pool
the campfire

5. our campsite
last day of school

6. Dad's big catch!
Sam's new dog

At Home: Cut pictures from a magazine. Then help your
child write captions for the photographs.

Write the answer to each question on the line.

1. Is this a boat or a bowl? _____

2. Is this toast or a toad? _____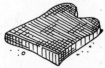

3. Is this a rod or a road? _____

4. Is this a pipe or a pillow? _____

5. Is this a window or a wing? _____

6. Is this a note or a notch? _____

7. Is this go or a goal? _____

8. Is this a cot or a coat? _____

© Macmillan/McGraw-Hill

At Home: Help your child write a story about a toad in a hole. Use as many long *o* and short *o* words as you can.

Say the words. Then listen to the **long i** sound.

ch**i**ld   fl**y**   h**igh**

Write the word that completes the sentence.

_____

- - - - - - - - - - - - - - - -

1. Meg's kite will _____ over the trees.

try   fly   cry

- - - - - - - - - - - - - - - -

2. Mike will _____ up his new truck.

win   wind   white

_____

- - - - - - - - - - - - - - - -

3. We eat lunch together on a _____ hill.

might   high   fly

_____

- - - - - - - - - - - - - - - -

4. Let's wave to that plane in the _____.

my   sky   cry

_____

- - - - - - - - - - - - - - - -

5. The _____ can walk to his house.

mild   child   cut

At Home: With your child, write some sentences with words
that contain the long *i* sound. Use *i, y,* or *igh.*

© Macmillan/McGraw-Hill

Write the letter of the word from the box that completes each sentence.

a. head	**b.** never	**c.** should	**d.** ball
e. shout	**f.** laughter	**g.** meadow	**h.** Perhaps

_____
- - - - - -

1. The boys and girls _____ for the team.

_____
- - - - - -

2. The big kite was flying high over Kim's _____.

_____
- - - - - -

3. Ben is _____ late for the school bus.

_____
- - - - - -

4. There was a lot of _____ at the show.

_____
- - - - - -

5. We _____ get a new bat and _____ at the shop.

_____
- - - - - -

6. _____ we can ride together in the green _____ today.

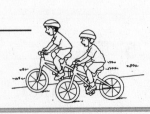

At Home: Have your child choose one picture and write another sentence to describe it. Encourage the use of some of the words from the box.

© Macmillan/McGraw-Hill

Name _____

As you read <u>The Kite</u>, fill in the Problem and Solution Chart.

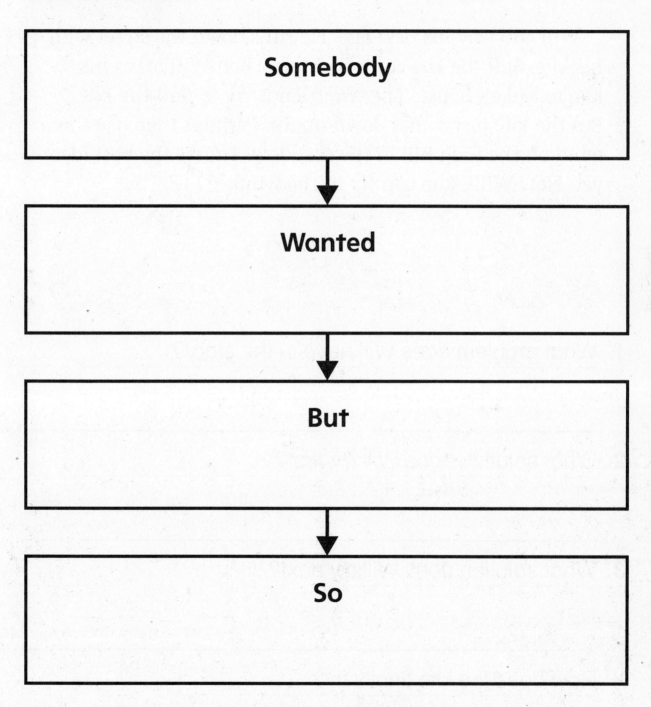

Somebody

↓

Wanted

↓

But

↓

So

How does the Problem and Solution Chart help you better understand <u>The Kite</u>?

 At Home: Have your child use the chart to retell the story.

© Macmillan/McGraw-Hill

Name _____

Read the story about Will's <u>problem</u> and <u>solution</u>. Then answer the questions.

Will can't fly his new kite. He runs down the street with his kite. Still the kite can't fly high. Then Will takes his kite to Mike's house. The two friends try to pull the kite. But the kite just comes down again. Perhaps there is more wind on the high hill in the meadow. That is the best idea yet. Now Will's kite can fly in the wind.

1. What problem does Will have in the story?

_____

_____

2. What solution does Will try first?

_____

_____

3. What solution does Will try next?

_____

_____

4. How does the kite finally fly?

_____

_____

At Home: Have your child describe a problem at home or at school and the steps taken to solve it.

© Macmillan/McGraw-Hill

Name _____

As I read, I will pay attention to the dialogue.

	"That box is for me," Nick shouted. "I
8	can take it now." Gus went on his way.
17	Sky looked at the big, big box. "You will never
27	lift that box," Sky said.
32	"So I will try to push it," Nick said. "Perhaps I
43	should try to pull it, too?"
49	But the box never moved. Nick was too little
58	and the box was so big.
64	"I can not do this myself. I need you, Sky," said
75	Nick. "This needs a push and a pull."
83	Nick and Sky worked together. Just then flakes
91	of snow fell. Nick and Sky woke up. 99

Comprehension Check

1. Why can't Nick move the box?

2. How do Nick and Sky move the box?

	Words Read	–	Number of Errors	=	Words Correct Score
First Read		–		=	
Second Read		–		=	

© Macmillan/McGraw-Hill

At Home: Help your child read the passage, paying attention to the goal at the top of the page.

The Kite • **Book 1.5/Unit 5**   **187**

Name _____

Practice

Vocabulary Strategy:
Word Parts

A verb is a word that shows action. When a verb has the ending **–ed**, the action happened in the past. The **–ing** ending means the action is happening now. You can pick out the word parts of a verb to figure out its meaning.

Underline the word in each sentence that has a word ending. Circle the base word. Then write <u>now</u> if it is something that is happening now. Write <u>past</u> if it was something that happened in the past.

1. I am playing with my best friend. _____

2. My cat climbed up the tree. _____

3. Dad milked a cow. _____

4. I am packing for my trip. _____

5. We watched a good game. _____

© Macmillan/McGraw-Hill

At Home: Talk about three things you did yesterday. Pay attention to the verbs that end in *–ed*.

To add **-er** or **-est** to words that end in **e**, drop the **e** and then add **-er** or **-est**.

cut**e** + **er** = cut**er**   That pup is **cuter** than this one.

cut**e** + **est** = cut**est**   The cat is the **cutest** of all.

Add -er or -est to each word. Then write the new word in the sentence.

_____
- -
1. His pet is _____ than the wild cat.
tame

_____
- -
2. The tree in the meadow is the _____.
large

_____
- -
3. My dad is the _____ of all.
brave

_____
- -
4. The _____ bus should stop here.
late

_____
- -
5. Now my dog is _____ than your dog.
clean

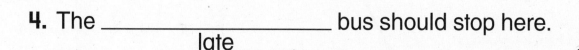

At Home: Have your child add *-er* and *-est* to one of the following words: *wide, ripe, pale.* Then ask your child to use the word in a sentence.

Name _____

Look at the diagram of a fire truck. Use the words from the box to complete the diagram. Write the words of the correct labels.

| ladder | light | hose | cab |

_____
- - - - - - - - - - - - - - - -

1. _____   _____
- - - - - - - - - - - - - - - -   - - - - - - - - - - - - - - - -

2. _____   3. _____

_____
- - - - - - - - - - - - - - - -

4. _____

At Home: Have your child write another thing that is the same and another thing that is different about Kim and Kate.

Name _____

Say the words. Listen to the sounds.

long i	**short i**
tight **cr**y m**i**ld	s**i**t

Circle the word that completes each sentence.

1. The _____ wanted to play in the ball game.

    chin   child   chill

2. Sam went home with his new pup _____ away.

    right   ride   rid

3. Perhaps we can _____ the kite in the meadow.

    fit   flight   fly

4. Max _____ a very ripe grape.

    bit   bite   by

5. The _____ cat likes to hide in the bush.

    win   wild   wind

6. The boys and girls can skate in the _____
    after school.   right   rid   rink

At Home: Have your child write other sentences with words
that contain long *i* spelled *i, y,* and *igh* and short *i* spelled *i*.

Together the letters **a** and **r** stand for the sound you hear in **car.** Listen for the **ar** sound in the word.

car

Read the sentence. Then write the word that completes the sentence.

1. We can play in the back _____.

yard
yarn

2. The _____ is far away.

smart
star
start

3. The _____ has many teeth.

shark

4. Wheat grows on a _____.

farm
barn

5. A _____ is a fish.

cart
carp

6. Nana gave me a blue _____.

scar
scarf

At Home: Challenge your child to write other *ar* words, such as *far, park, tar, bark.*

© Macmillan/McGraw-Hill

Name _____

| question | better | children | discovery |
| machine | or | round | |

Use a word from the box to complete each sentence.

_____

Some _____ worked together to

make a _____ that could help.

It was big and _____. It was a

_____ way to take things to school.

It could hold your backpack _____ your

lunch. The machine could also answer any

_____.

What a great _____!

At Home: Help your child write a story using the words *machine* and *discovery*.

Kids' Inventions
Book 1.5/Unit 5

193

© Macmillan/McGraw-Hill

As you read <u>Kids' Inventions</u>, fill in the
Cause and Effect Chart.

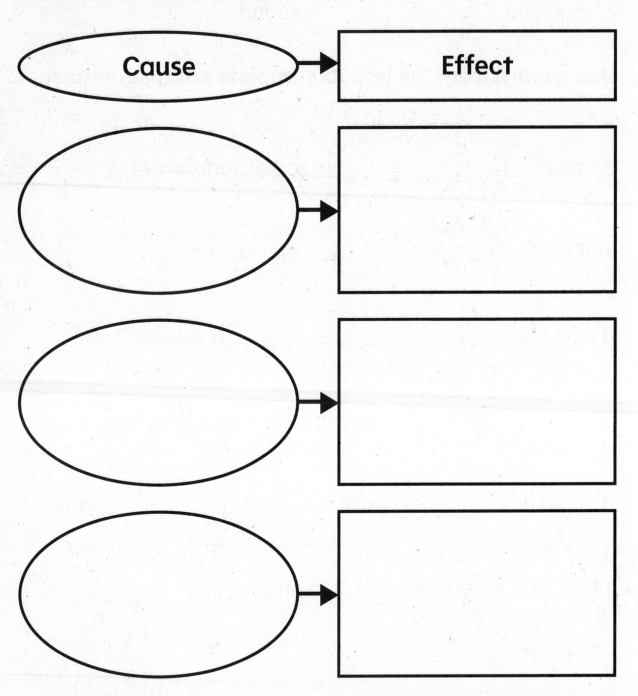

How does the Cause and Effect Chart help you better
understand <u>Kids' Inventions</u>?

At Home: Have your child use the chart to retell the story.

© Macmillan/McGraw-Hill

Name _____

The **cause** is why something happens.
The **effect** is what happens.

cause   effect

Match the cause to the effect.

1. The dog had a bath.

2. The girl fell.

3. Bob stepped on the box.

4. The tire is flat.

5. Ben ran faster than the others.

6. It is raining.

At Home: Fold a piece of paper in half. Then have your child
draw a cause on one half and an effect on the other half.

Name _____

Practice

Vocabulary Strategy: Dictionary

Words with the same or almost the same meaning are **synonyms**. You can use a **dictionary** or a **thesaurus** to find synonyms. A **thesaurus** is a book that lists synonyms.

build to make something: Tim will **build** a house.

Synonyms: construct, make, create, form, and put together: Tim will **construct** a house.

Circle the two synonyms in each row that could complete the sentence.

I. That inventor has a clever _____.

broken   invention   creation

2. The robot can _____.

speak   paper   talk

3. The robot won a _____ in the contest.

prize   box   award

First Prize

At Home: Think of two synonyms for *funny*. Write a sentence using *funny*. Say the sentence using the synonyms.

Name _____

As I read, I will pay attention to questions in the passage.

Who Were the Wright Brothers?

5	Orville and Wilbur Wright were inventors.
11	Their dream was to build a flying machine.
19	As children, they liked to find out how things
28	worked. As grownups, they worked in a bike
36	shop.
37	In 1900, the Wright brothers built a glider with
45	two wings. Each wing was covered with cloth.
53	They flew their glider like a kite.
60	After testing the glider, one brother got on the
69	glider. Then he would glide in the air.
77	The Wright brothers made and tested many
84	gliders. With each new discovery they made a
92	better glider. 94

Comprehension Check

1. Describe the glider the Wright brothers built.

2. How did the brothers fly their glider?

	Words Read	−	Number of Errors	=	Words Correct Score
First Read		−		=	
Second Read		−		=	

At Home: Help your child read the passage, paying attention to the goal at the top of the page.

Name _____

A **card catalog** helps you find books in a library.

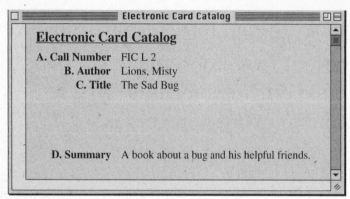

Electronic Card Catalog	
A. Call Number	FIC L 2
B. Author	Lions, Misty
C. Title	The Sad Bug
D. Summary	A book about a bug and his helpful friends.

A: These numbers show where you can find the book in the library.

B: author's name

C: the title of the book

D: what the book is about

Look at the computer screen. Then answer the questions.

1. What is the title? _____

2. What is the book about?

_____

_____

3. Who is the author? _____

4. Where can you find this book in the library? _____

© Macmillan/McGraw-Hill

At Home: Give your child an index card. Then help him or her to make a card catalog page for a favorite book.

Name _____

An **abbreviation** is a short form of writing a longer word.

Look at these abbreviations.

Mister → Mr.   Saturday → Sat.   Doctor → Dr.

Write the abbreviations for each word.

1. Doctor _____

2. Saturday _____

3. Mister _____

Read each sentence. Then circle the word that matches each abbreviation.

4. I will make a cake on <u>Sat.</u>

   September   Saturday   Sunday

5. <u>Dr.</u> Shin helps me when I'm sick.

   Doctor   Saturday   Mister

6. We sent mail to <u>Mr.</u> Lee.

   Doctor   Saturday   Mister

At Home: Help your child write a letter to an adult. Then help him or her write the correct abbreviation.

Name _____

Circle the answer to each question.

1. Does a shark have a tail?   yes no

2. Does a car go on a rail?   yes no

3. Can a star rain?   yes no

4. Does a man have an arm?   yes no

5. Can a farm have a gate?   yes no

6. Can a scarf bark?   yes no

7. Is a rake sharp?   yes no

8. Does a park have a tail?   yes no

Then circle the words with the ar sound as in <u>far</u>. Write the words below.

_____

- -

_____

- -

_____

At Home: Let your child choose one of the sentences to illustrate.

Name _____

The letters **or** stand for the middle sound in **horse**.

Circle the word that completes the sentence. Then write the word on the line.

_____

1. The _____ is in the barn.

   porch   horse   fort

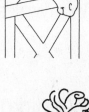

_____

2. The _____ is sharp.

   storm   stork   thorn

_____

3. We play _____ at the park.

   sports   shorts   sort

_____

4. The lamp has a new _____.

   cord   fork   corn

_____

5. We can patch the _____ pants.

   north   torn   for

© Macmillan/McGraw-Hill

🏠 **At Home:** Help your child to write sentences using words from above that have the *or* sound.

Whistle for Willie • **Book 1.5/Unit 5**   **201**

Name _____

Use a word from the box to complete each sentence.

early	along	suddenly	errand
nothing	thought	instead	

1. We woke up _____ this morning.

2. We did an _____ for Mom.

3. There was _____ in the rice jar.

4. Mr. Ford _____ he had some.

5. We gave him three roses _____.

6. _____, it started to rain.

7. Mr. Ford told us to run _____.

At Home: Have your child draw a picture to illustrate one or two of the sentences.

© Macmillan/McGraw-Hill

As you read <u>Whistle for Willie</u>, fill in the Inference Chart.

Text Clues	What You Know	Inferences

How does the Inference Chart help you better understand <u>Whistle for Willie</u>?

At Home: Have your child use the chart to retell the story.

Look at the picture. Then underline the sentence that is true.

1.

Mark likes to play ball.

Mark wins the race.

Mark likes to ride his bike.

2.

I can play catch.

I can see far away.

I can sing and dance.

3.

I can play a game.

I can help Dad.

I can read a good book.

4.

The water is fun.

The water is not deep.

The water is too cold.

5.

I don't like to help.

I can help Mom make pancakes.

I don't know how to make pancakes.

At Home: Together, draw a picture of something your child can do. Then have your child label the picture "I can do it."

As I read, I will pay attention to the punctuation.

	Early one day, Jill tried to tie her shoelaces.
9	But she could not tie them.
15	"You will be able to do it one day soon,"
25	said Jill's mother. "Put on your shoes with the
34	straps instead." Then she left to do an errand.
43	Along came Jill's sister, Molly. "Pretend the
50	laces are snakes. Tie the snakes together, like
58	this," said Molly.
61	Jill kept getting her snakes tied in knots.
69	"Put on your sandals," said Molly. "They do
77	not have laces."
80	Jill sat down and tried again. 86

Comprehension Check

1. What is Jill trying to do?

2. What animals does Molly tell Jill to pretend her shoelaces are?

	Words Read	–	Number of Errors	=	Words Correct Score
First Read		–		=	
Second Read		–		=	

At Home: Help your child read the passage, paying attention to the goal at the top of the page.

A **base word** is the word that is left when you remove the **-ed** or **-ing** ending. You can use the base word to figure out the meaning of a word.

The teacher is **forming** the clay.
The base word is **form.**
   form to give shape to something

Write the base word.

1. moved   moving   _____

2. listening   listened   _____

3. crashed   crashing   _____

4. whistled   whistling   _____

5. baked   baking   _____

© Macmillan/McGraw-Hill

At Home: Say three sentences using the words *move,* *moved,* and *moving.*

Name _____

If a verb ends in a **consonant + y,** change the **y**
to **i** before adding **ed**.   cr**y** + ed = cr**i**ed

Write the word that completes each sentence.

_____
- - - - - - - - - - - - - -

1. The baby _____.

cried   cryed

_____
- - - - - - - - - - - - - -

2. Han _____ his hands.

dryed   dried

_____
- - - - - - - - - - - - - -

3. Mom _____ the top open.

pried   pryed

_____
- - - - - - - - - - - - - -

4. Kelly _____ the big bike.

tried   tryed

_____
- - - - - - - - - - - - - -

5. Dad _____ the fish.

fryed   fried

 At Home: Have your child write and illustrate a sentence
about something he or she has tried.

A **graph** can show how many of something.

Read the bar graph. Then answer the questions.

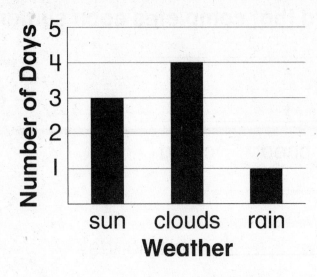

1. How many days were sunny? _____

2. How many days were cloudy? _____

3. How many days were rainy? _____

4. How many more days had sun than had rain? _____

At Home: Have your child draw a picture of something he or she likes to do on a rainy day.

© Macmillan/McGraw-Hill

Name _____

The letters **or** stand for the middle sound in **born**.

The letters **ar** stand for the middle sound in **barn**.

Circle the word that completes each sentence. Then write the word on the line.

1. Grandpa and I are on the _____.

porch   part   parch

2. It is _____.

dorm   fork   dark

3. We see many _____.

stores   stars   cars

4. They are bright but _____.

for   farm   far

5. Grandpa shows me the _____ star.

barn   north   short

At Home: Have your child sort the words to make an *or* list and an *ar* list.

Whistle for Willie • **Book 1.5/Unit 5**   **209**

© Macmillan/McGraw-Hill

The letters **er, ir,** and **ur** stand for the same sound.

cl**er**k   b**ir**d   t**ur**n

Circle the word that names the picture. Then write the word on the line.

1.
girl
gull

_____

2.
cot
curl

_____

3.
fun
fern

_____

4.
spur
spot

_____

5.
hid
her

_____

6.
squirt
squint

_____

At Home: Have your child read and spell the *er, ir,* and *ur* words.

Read the clues. Use words from the box to fill in the puzzle.

animals	beautiful	crowded	from
part	places	tiny	

Across

3. too many

4. pig, hen, seal

5. You can visit these.

6. not big

Down

1. to Jake, _____ Dad

2. The roses look _____.

5. not all

At Home: Ask your child what each word means.

As you read <u>A Fruit is a Suitcase for Seeds</u>, fill in the Classify and Categorize Chart

Classify and Categorize	
One Seed	**Many Seeds**

How does the Classify and Categorize Chart help you better understand <u>A Fruit is a Suitcase for Seeds</u>?

At Home: Have your child use the chart to retell the story.

Cross out the word that does not belong in each group.

1. seed   house   leaf   plant

2. wind   rain   sun   cat

3. tree   rock   grass   rose

4. sleep   jump   run   walk

5. speak   sing   yell   fly

6. school   house   road   shop

7. dog   bike   cat   bird

8. bad   nice   fine   good

Think of two more groups of three words that belong together. Write them on the line.

9. _____

10. _____

At Home: Ask your child to explain why a word is crossed out and why the other words go together.

A Fruit Is a Suitcase for Seeds
Book 1.5/Unit 5
213

As I read, I will pay attention to patterns in the story.

Strawberries are easy plants to grow.

6 | 1. First find a place that gets at least six hours
16 | of sun.
18 | 2. Next dig holes for the little plants. Put the
27 | holes 12 inches apart. They should not be
34 | crowded together.
36 | 3. Put the plants in the holes. Press the soil
45 | around each plant. Make sure the soil covers
53 | the tops of the roots.
58 | 4. Next water the plants.
62 | 5. Pick the strawberries when they are ripe.
69 | Animals like strawberries. As your plants grow,
76 | you will need to watch for animals. Birds, turtles,
85 | and bugs eat strawberry plants. 90

Comprehension Check

1. Is it easy or hard to grow strawberries?

2. What do strawberries need to grow?

	Words Read	–	Number of Errors	=	Words Correct Score
First Read		–		=	
Second Read		–		=	

© Macmillan/McGraw-Hill

At Home: Help your child read the passage, paying attention to the goal at the top of the page.

Context clues are words that help you figure out the meaning of a new word. Context clues may be found in the same sentence or in nearby sentences.

Use context clues to figure out the meaning of the underlined word. Fill in the correct circle.

1. The man <u>displays</u> the fruit. He wants to set the melon on the shelf.

   ○ throws away

   ○ shows or sets out

2. Jordan likes to go places. He <u>enjoys</u> taking the bus to the fruit stand.

   ○ likes

   ○ twists

3. Jordan's mom likes to <u>relax</u> at the park. She likes to sit and read.

   ○ finish quickly

   ○ rest

© Macmillan/McGraw-Hill

At Home: Talk about items you like to pack into a suitcase when you go on vacation.

A Fruit Is a Suitcase for Seeds
Book 1.5/Unit 5 215

> A **prefix** is a word part you can add to the beginning of a base word to change the meaning of the word.
>
> The prefix **re-** means **again**: re + pack = **re**pack.
>
> The prefix **un-** means **not** or **the opposite**: **un** + pack = **un**pack.

Write the meaning of each of the following words:

1. reuse _____

2. refill _____

3. unhappy _____

4. unsafe _____

5. remake _____

6. untrue _____

At Home: Work with your child to make up a sentence for each word.

© Macmillan/McGraw-Hill

Name _____

Some poems have a **rhyming pattern**.

In some poems, the second line of a verse rhymes with the fourth line.

A. Circle the two rhyming words in each poem.

The sun is out.

What a fine day!

Will you come out with me

And play?

I saw a seed

Fall to the ground.

It never made

A sound.

You want to play ball,

But what I'd like

Is to ride round and round

On my brand new bike.

I look up at

The sky at night,

And watch the stars

That shine so bright.

B. Think of more rhyming pairs. Write the pairs below.

1. _____ _____

2. _____ _____

© Macmillan/McGraw-Hill

At Home: Ask your child to think of more pairs of rhyming words.

A Fruit Is a Suitcase for Seeds
Book 1.5/Unit 5

217

Name _____

Write the letters <u>ar</u>, <u>or</u>, <u>er</u>, <u>ur</u>, or <u>ir</u> to finish each picture name. Then color the pictures that have the same vowel sound as in <u>girl</u>.

1.

b ___ ___ n

2.

s h ___ ___ k

3.

s k ___ ___ t

4.

f ___ ___ n

5.

c ___ ___ n

6.

s c ___ ___ f

At Home: Ask your child to spell the name of each picture.

Name _____

Write the word from the box that has the same meaning.

1. boys and girls _____

2. very little _____

3. dad _____

4. yell _____

5. just then _____

6. too many people _____

7. not all _____

8. sheep, dog, pig _____

father

children

tiny

suddenly

shout

part

animals

crowded

Use a word from the box to complete each sentence.

| errand   better   try   early   laughter   never |

_____

----

1. Today Mark feels _____.

_____

----

2. We should _____ to plant corn.

_____

----

3. After the joke, Dora heard _____.

_____

----

4. You should _____ shout in the car.

_____

----

5. Go to the store to do an _____.

_____

----

6. I get up _____ in the morning.

Write a sentence for the word <u>round</u>.

_____

_____

Use words from the box to complete the sentences.

cow	mouse	crown	clown
out	round	shout	

1. The king had a gold _____ on his head.

2. The ball was red and _____.

3. We can't go _____ to play if it is raining.

4. The brown _____ lives on a farm.

5. "Don't _____ at me," yelled Ben.

6. The cat ran after the little _____.

7. The funny _____ had a red nose and big feet.

At Home: Have your child write a sentence for each of the following words: *town*, *proud*, *couch*, and *now*.

Dot and Jabber and the Big Bug Mystery • **Book 1.5/Unit 6**

221

© Macmillan/McGraw-Hill

Name _____

**Circle the word that completes each sentence.
Then write the word on the line.**

_____
- - - - - - - - - - - - - - - - - - - -

1. Where has the cat _____?

                       done   gone

_____
- - - - - - - - - - - - - - - - - - - -

2. The girls have _____ best friends
for years.   been   are

_____
- - - - - - - - - - - - - - - - - - - -

3. Let's keep _____ for the missing dog.

        sending   searching

_____
- - - - - - - - - - - - - - - - - - - -

4. We must look for _____.

           close   clues

_____
- - - - - - - - - - - - - - - - - - - -

5. I can't see it. It must be _____.

         invisible   instead

_____
- - - - - - - - - - - - - - - - - - - -

6. "The keys are in my _____ purse,"
said Mom.   over   other

At Home: Have your child complete this sentence starter:
If I were invisible for a day, I would _____.

Name _____

As you read <u>Dot and Jabber and the Big Bug Mystery</u>, fill in the Illustrations Chart.

Use Illustrations	
Illustration	**What It Shows**

How does the Illustrations Chart help you better understand <u>Dot and Jabber and the Big Bug Mystery</u>?

At Home: Have your child use the chart to retell the story.

Read each description. Then follow the directions.

1. Birds have beaks. Birds gather food with their beaks. Beaks can be different colors. Draw a beak on the bird.

2. Fish have fins. Fins help a fish swim. This fish has a blue tail fin. Draw the tail fin on the fish.

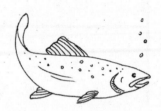

3. Cats have four legs, a tail, and soft fur. They also have whiskers. Cats use their whiskers to sense things. Draw the whiskers on the cat.

4. Spiders spin webs. They trap food in their webs. Spiders have 2 body parts and 8 legs. Draw the legs on the spider.

5. Ants dig tunnels underground. They have 6 legs and 3 body parts. They also have 2 antennae, or feelers, on their heads. Draw the antennae on the ant.

© Macmillan/McGraw-Hill

At Home: Look through books about animals and talk about the illustrations.

As I read, I will pay attention to the exclamation points.

	"Look at all the butterflies!" I said to Amy.
9	"I hope I find a Painted Lady!"
16	"Is that one?" Amy asked.
21	"No," I said. "A Painted Lady is orange."
29	A butterfly landed on Amy.
34	"Look, Sara!" Amy said. "Is it a Painted Lady?"
43	"No," I said. " A Painted Lady doesn't have
51	black bands."
53	"I have never been here before," I said to a
63	helper. "Do you have a Painted Lady?"
70	"Yes," she said. "Search! You will find one."
78	"There it is!" said Amy.
83	"No, it's not," I said. "A Painted Lady has
92	black and white spots." 96

Comprehension Check

1. What kind of butterfly are Amy and her friend hoping to find?

2. Does the butterfly have bands or spots?

	Words Read	–	Number of Errors	=	Words Correct Score
First Read		–		=	
Second Read		–		=	

At Home: Help your child read the passage, paying attention to the goal at the top of the page.

Dot and Jabber and the Big Bug Mystery • Book 1.5/Unit 6

225

> **pretends** plays or makes-believe: Danny **pretends** he is an astronaut.
>
> **vanished** disappeared: The sun **vanished** when the clouds came out.
>
> **observes** sees or notices: A scientist **observes** things under a microscope.
>
> **inspecting** looking at carefully: Mom is **inspecting** the house for dust.

Use a word from above to complete each sentence.

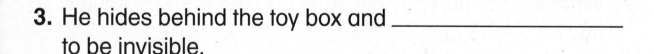

1. Kate thinks Matt _____ from the room!

2. She is _____ the room for clues.

3. He hides behind the toy box and _____ to be invisible.

4. Kate _____ many clues. She solves the mystery of the missing brother!

At Home: Ask your child to use each word in a sentence.

© Macmillan/McGraw-Hill

Name _____

A **syllable** is a part of a word.

Put the two syllables together. Write the word on the line. Then match the word to the picture it names.

1. kit   ten   _____

2. mag   net   _____

3. bas   ket   _____

4. ham   mer   _____

Divide each word into two syllables. Then write each syllable.

rabbit   pencil

_____ _____   _____ _____

At Home: Write the word parts above on separate cards and play a matching game with them.

Dot and Jabber and the Big Bug Mystery • **Book 1.5/Unit 6**   **227**

Name _____

A **head** tells what information is in a section of an article or story.

Read the article about spiders.

Spiders

A spider is a small animal. A spider can be black, red, brown, or even yellow.

The Body of a Spider

A spider has 2 body parts. It also has 8 legs. An insect has only 6 legs.

The Home of a Spider

A spider lives in a web. It spins a sticky web. When a bug flies into the web, it gets stuck. Then the spider eats it.

Answer the questions about the article.

1. Circle the two heads that tell what information is in the sections.

2. Write one fact from each section.

_____

_____

_____

_____

At Home: Have your child tell you about spiders, such as what they look like and what they eat.

Circle the word that names each picture. Then write the word.

1.

burn   bird

_____

- - - - - - - - - - -

_____

2.

mouse   most

_____

- - - - - - - - - - -

_____

3.

hose   house

_____

- - - - - - - - - - -

_____

4.

town   toad

_____

- - - - - - - - - - -

_____

5.

stir   star

_____

- - - - - - - - - - -

_____

6.

bone   boat

_____

- - - - - - - - - - -

_____

7.

owl   own

_____

- - - - - - - - - - -

_____

8.

crowd   crown

_____

- - - - - - - - - - -

_____

At Home: Have your child write a sentence for each word not circled.

Use words from the box to name the pictures.

book	cook	look	foot
woof	wool	hook	hood

1. _____

2. _____

3. _____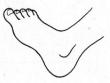

4. _____

5. _____

6. _____

7. _____

8. _____

At Home: Ask your child to use each word in a sentence.

Use a word from the box to complete each sentence. Then look in the sentences for other words from the box. Circle them.

birds	Earth	table	bear
fooling	guess	helmet	space

1. They can see Earth from outer

_____

- - - - - - - - - - - - - - - - -

_____ .

_____

- - - - - - - - - - - - - - - - -

2. Her book and bike _____

are on the table.

3. He read a story about tiny birds and

_____

- - - - - - - - - - - - - - - - -

a huge _____ .

4. I guess they just like

_____

- - - - - - - - - - - - - - - - -

_____ around.

© Macmillan/McGraw-Hill

🏠 **At Home:** Have your child use two of the words
to write another sentence.

Little Bear Goes to the
Moon • **Book 1.5/Unit 6**   **231**

As you read Little Bear Goes to the Moon, fill in the Predictions Chart.

What I Predict	What Happens

How does the Predictions Chart help you better understand Little Bear Goes to the Moon?

At Home: Have your child use the chart to retell the story.

© Macmillan/McGraw-Hill

Name _____

In a **prediction** you tell what you think will happen next.

Read each story. Then complete the sentence to tell what could happen next.

1. The ship takes off. It is flying to the moon.
It will

_____

- -

_____.

2. The car is not clean. Mom drives to the
car wash. The car will

_____

- -

_____.

3. It is a windy day. We have kites.
We will

_____

- -

_____.

4. Dad brings home a bag full of food.
He cooks the food. We will

_____

- -

_____.

© Macmillan/McGraw-Hill

At Home: Ask your child to predict what will happen
next in each story and draw a picture of one of them.

As I read, I will pay attention to pauses for sentence punctuation.

	Bird and Bear sat at the lake.
7	It was night, and they were looking at the
16	moon.
17	"The moon looks flat," said Bird.
23	"But I know it is round like a ball."
32	"I would love to fly to the moon," said Bear.
42	"You're fooling. You can't fly!" said Bird.
49	"I could make a spaceship," said Bear.
56	"Then I could fly."
60	"Ha!" said Bird. "That would take too long.
68	I could fly to the moon and be back before
78	you are done."
81	"You can't fly to the moon," said Bear.
89	"It's too far away in space." 95

Comprehension Check

1. How will Bear fly to the moon?

2. How will Bird fly to the moon?

	Words Read	–	Number of Errors	=	Words Correct Score
First Read		–		=	
Second Read		–		=	

© Macmillan/McGraw-Hill

At Home: Help your child read the passage, paying attention to the goal at the top of the page.

Name _____

> **Context clues** are words that help you figure out the meaning of a new word. Context clues may be found in the same sentence or in nearby sentences.

Fill in the circle next to the correct meaning of the bold word. Use the <u>underlined</u> context clues to figure out the meaning of each word.

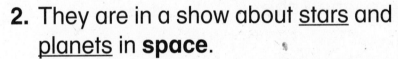

1. The girls are <u>giggling</u> and **fooling** around on the stage.

   ○ acting silly   ○ cleaning

2. They are in a show about <u>stars</u> and <u>planets</u> in **space**.

   ○ the beach   ○ a place where astronauts travel

3. The big **helmet** <u>hides</u> most of Seta's <u>face</u>.

   ○ boots   ○ something that protects a person's head

4. Maria <u>fell</u> <u>down</u>. Her moon rocks **tumbled** <u>off</u> the <u>stage</u>.

   ○ dropped   ○ dug

5. "These space boots make it hard to <u>feel</u> the **earth** <u>under</u> my <u>feet</u>," said Seta.

   ○ cold water   ○ ground; also the planet where we live

© Macmillan/McGraw-Hill

At Home: Ask your child to make up sentences using two of the words in bold letters.

Name _____

Read the underlined words. Then write a word with -ful or -less that means the same.

1. They laughed and danced and sang. _____
They were <u>full of joy</u>.

2. The boy didn't think he would win. _____
He was <u>without hope</u>.

3. She took <u>a lot of care</u> when she _____
packed the dishes.

4. The lonely man did not know anyone. _____
He was <u>without a friend</u>.

Pick a word with -ful and a word with -less. Then write a sentence for each word.

5. _____

6. _____

Name _____

The **question and answer format** uses the words
question and **answer** to show who is speaking.

Question: How does it feel? **Answer:** It feels like flying!

Who is speaking?

Draw a line from the sentence to show who is speaking.

1.

Question: Is it raining out?   **Answer:** Yes, it is.

2.

Question: What did you find? **Answer:** I found a chest!

At Home: Have your child "interview" a family member
about his or her day. Help your child phrase questions. Then
write the interview together. Use the question/answer format.

Use two words from the box to complete each sentence.

found	book	couch	frown	shook	wood
clown	crown	hook	round	good	hood

1. The _____ has a _____.

2. The _____ table is _____.

3. The coat with a _____ hangs on a _____.

4. The _____ is on the _____.

5. I _____ my _____ dog.

At Home: Have your child read each sentence aloud. Encourage him or her to act out one or two sentences.

© Macmillan/McGraw-Hill

The letters **oo** can stand for the middle sound in m**oo**n.

Read the word and circle the picture for it.

1. noon

2. zoo

3. school

4. spoon

5. groom

© Macmillan/McGraw-Hill

Use the words in the box to complete each sentence.

| only   laugh   goes   ever   ordinary   interesting |

_____

- - - - - - - - - - - - - - - - -

1. People like to _____.

_____

- - - - - - - - - - - - - - - - -

2. It eats _____ the leaf.

_____

- - - - - - - - - - - - - - - - -

3. She _____ in.

_____

- - - - - - - - - - - - - - - - -

4. This bird is _____.

_____

- - - - - - - - - - - - - - - - -

5. This bird is more _____.

_____

- - - - - - - - - - - - - - - - -

6. Do you _____ work outside?

At Home: Have your child write a sentence using two of the words in the box.

As you read <u>Cool Jobs</u>, fill in the Classify and Catagorize Chart.

Classify and Categorize	
Jobs to Make Things	**Jobs That Help**

How does the Classify and Catagorize Chart help you better understand <u>Cool Jobs</u>?

 At Home: Have your child use the chart to retell the story.

Cool Jobs • **Book 1.5/Unit 6** 241

Sort the words into two groups.

cow	girls	children	bear	men
boys	frog	mother	snake	bird

People

_____

- - - - - - - - - - - - - - - - -

_____

_____

- - - - - - - - - - - - - - - - -

_____

_____

- - - - - - - - - - - - - - - - -

_____

_____

- - - - - - - - - - - - - - - - -

_____

Animals

_____

- - - - - - - - - - - - - - - - -

_____

_____

- - - - - - - - - - - - - - - - -

_____

_____

- - - - - - - - - - - - - - - - -

_____

_____

- - - - - - - - - - - - - - - - -

_____

At Home: Have your child add another item
to each category.

Name _____

Practice

Vocabulary Strategy:
Thesaurus

Words with opposite meanings are **antonyms**.
You can use a thesaurus to find an antonym.

Antonyms are listed after the synonyms.

loud   noisy, roaring   Antonym: **quiet**

small   little, tiny   Antonym: **big**

Write a sentence for each set of antonyms.

1. break   fix

_____

- -

_____

2. sweet   sour

_____

- -

_____

3. many   few

_____

- -

_____

4. dirty   clean

_____

- -

_____

At Home: Draw a picture to go with one of the
pairs of antonyms.

Cool Jobs • **Book 1.5/Unit 6**   **243**

As I read, I will pay attention to pauses for sentence punctuation.

	Some pilots fly sightseeing planes.
5	Sightseeing planes fly low to the ground.
12	That way the people on the plane can see all
22	the sights.
24	Some pilots fly helicopters. A helicopter is
31	different from an ordinary plane. Helicopter
37	pilots can fly forward and fly backward.
44	They also can turn the helicopter in a circle
53	and stay still in the air.
59	There are places where only helicopters
65	can fly. They are places where ordinary
72	planes cannot go. 75

Comprehension Check

1. Why do sightseeing planes fly low to the ground?

2. In what directions do helicopter pilots have to fly?

	Words Read	–	Number of Errors	=	Words Correct Score
First Read		–		=	
Second Read		–		=	

At Home: Help your child read the passage, paying attention to the goal at the top of the page.

Name _____

You can use the Internet to find out about a topic.
Put important or key words in the search box.
Then hit **GO** and a list of links will pop up.

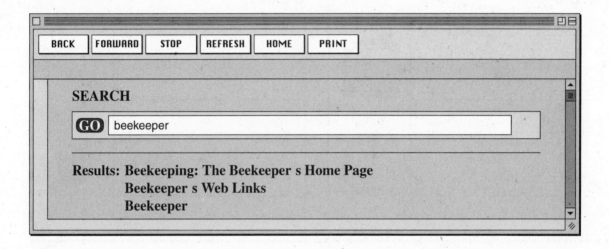

| BACK | FORWARD | STOP | REFRESH | HOME | PRINT |

SEARCH

GO beekeeper

Results: Beekeeping: The Beekeeper s Home Page
      Beekeeper s Web Links
      Beekeeper

Write the key words you would type in the search box to look up the following:

1. You want to know more
about the moon.

_____
_____

2. You want to find out about
places to see in New York.

_____
_____

3. You want to know more about
the animal you like best.

_____
_____

4. You want to find out about
a job you would like.

_____
_____

© Macmillan/McGraw-Hill

At Home: If possible, help your child search one of the
above topics. If no computer is available, have your child list
three topics he or she would like to research.

Change or add one letter to each word to make a new word. Use the pictures to help.

moo

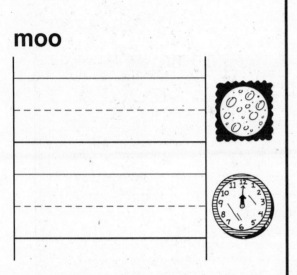

soon

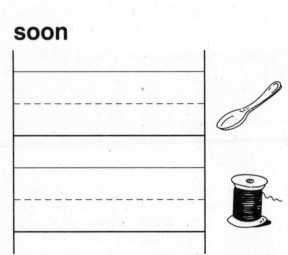

too

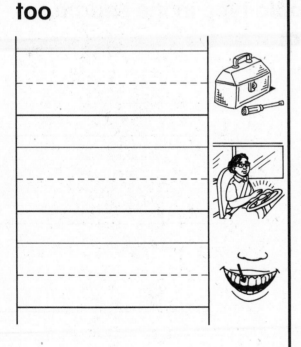

roof

At Home: Have your child make up sentences using two or more words from each box.

Name _____

Complete each sentence with a word from the box. Then underline any words that have <u>ou</u>, <u>ow</u>, or <u>oo</u>.

| foot | round | stoop | cow | brook | root |

1. An animal that says "moo" is a _____.

2. When you bend down, you _____.

3. A boot goes on your _____.

4. A scoop of ice cream is _____.

5. The underground part of a plant is a _____.

6. A small stream is a _____.

At Home: Have your child think of words that rhyme with words in the box.

Cool Jobs • Book 1.5/Unit 6   247

Name _____

Read the words. What vowel sound do you hear? The letters **au** and **aw** stand for the vowel sound in P**au**l and p**aw**.

Circle the word that answers each riddle.

1. I am a large bird.

What am I?   hawk   haul

2. I grabbed with my claw.

What did I do?   call   caught

3. This is the start of the day.

What is it?   dorm   dawn

4. I like to do this in art class.

What is it?   draw   drink

5. A bird cant use this to make a nest.

What is it?   stand   straw

At Home: Have your child make up another riddle about a hawk, another bird, or an animal.

Name _____

Choose a word from the box to finish each sentence. Then write the word on the line.

| wild   learn   enough   across   air   cub   eyes |

_____

- - - - - - - - - - - - - - - -

1. The tiger _____ has a sister.

_____

- - - - - - - - - - - - - - - - - -

2. Soon the cubs will be old _____ to hunt

_____

- - - - - - - - - - - - - -

in the _____ .

_____

- - - - - - - - - - - - - - - - -

3. They will _____ from their mother.

_____

- - - - - - - - - - - - - - - - - -

4. They like the night _____ .

_____

- - - - - - - - - - - - - - - - - -

5. Their _____ see well at night.

_____

- - - - - - - - - - - - - - - - - -

6. The cubs play, too. They swim _____ the stream.

At Home: Ask your child to draw a picture of a tiger cub and write a sentence about it.

As you read <u>A Tiger Cub Grows Up</u>, fill in the Compare and Contrast Chart.

Compare and Contrast	
Cub	**Grown-up**

How does the Compare and Contrast Chart help you better understand <u>A Tiger Cub Grows Up</u>?

At Home: Have your child use the chart to retell the story.

© Macmillan/McGraw-Hill

When you **compare**, you tell how two or more things are alike. When you **contrast**, you tell how things differ.

If something tells about "The Tiger," write it in that list. If something tells about "A Tiger Cub Grows Up," write it under that list. It is okay to write something under both.

lives in an animal park	speeds in the forest
has stripes	lives in the wild
poem real story	drinks milk

"The Tiger" by Douglas Florian

_____   _____

1. _____   2. _____

_____   _____

3. _____   4. _____

"A Tiger Cub Grows Up" by Joan Hewitt

_____   _____

5. _____   6. _____

_____   _____

7. _____   8. _____

At Home: Talk with your child about some things both tigers can do.

A Tiger Cub Grows Up
Book 1.5/Unit 6   251

As I read, I will pay attention to pausing for sentence punctuation.

	Some baby animals are called kids or cubs.
8	A baby horse is called a foal. Its mother is
18	called a mare. Less than an hour after it is
28	born, a foal will stand to drink milk. Foals
37	start to eat grass a few weeks after they are
47	born. Horses have very large eyes. They are
55	set on the sides of their heads. Horses have
64	short pointed ears. They can hear very well.
72	Horses also have a good sense of smell.
80	Horses have strong legs. They can kick their
88	legs in the air. 92

Comprehension Check

1. What is a baby horse called?

2. When does a foal stand up?

	Words Read	−	Number of Errors	=	Words Correct Score
First Read		−		=	
Second Read		−		=	

At Home: Help your child read the passage, paying attention to the goal at the top of the page.

An **inflected verb** is a verb with an ending. When you remove the **–ing** or **–ed** ending you are left with the base word.

inflected verb	base word
splash**ing**	splash
splash**ed**	splash

Write the ending. Then write the base word. The first one is done for you.

1. opened   _____ed_____   _____open_____

2. chewing   _____   _____

3. pointed   _____   _____

4. crawling   _____   _____

5. roaring   _____   _____

6. talked   _____   _____

© Macmillan/McGraw-Hill

At Home: As you read with your child, occasionally point out verbs ending in -*ed* and -*ing*. Ask your child to identify the base word.

The letters **au** and **aw** stand for the vowel sound in **Pau**l and **saw**.

Use the words in the box to complete the sentences.

saw   jaw   caught   lawn   taught

_____
1. Paul and Tawny play on the _____.

_____
2. Tawny _____ the ball.

_____
3. Paul _____ Tawny to get the ball.

_____
4. Tawny _____ the ball.

_____
5. She grabs it in her _____.

© Macmillan/McGraw-Hill

At Home: Sort the words into two lists. Label one list "Paul" words and the other list "Tawny" words. Then encourage your child to add other words to each list.

Poets often use words in funny and interesting ways. The sounds of words can help express their meaning.

Read the poem. Find the fun words in each verse. Then write the words on the lines.

BOW-WOW

Bow-wow says the dog,
Mew, mew says the cat,
Grunt, grunt goes the hog,
And squeak goes the rat.

Whoo-oo says the owl,
Caw, caw says the crow,
Quack, quack says the duck,
And what cuckoos say, you know.

A fine song I have made,
To please you, my dear;
And if it's well-sung,
'Twill be charming to hear.

_____

_____

_____

_____

At Home: Read the poem aloud. Then encourage your child to think of other fun words for the end of the first verse.

A Tiger Cub Grows Up
Book I.5/Unit 6

255

The letters **au** and **aw** stand for the vowel sound in h**au**l and p**aw**.

The letters **oo** can stand for the vowel sound in l**oo**k.

The letters **oo** can stand for the vowel sound in f**oo**d.

Circle the word that names the picture. Then write the word.

1. crawl
   cook

   _____

   - - - - - - - - - - - - - - -

2.  spoon
   spool

   _____

   - - - - - - - - - - - - - - -

3. paw
   yawn

   _____

   - - - - - - - - - - - - - - -

4. bone
   broom

   _____

   - - - - - - - - - - - - - - -

5.  book
   bag

   _____

   - - - - - - - - - - - - - - -

6.  fawn
   food

   _____

   - - - - - - - - - - - - - - -

 At Home: Sort the words into three groups: the same vowel sound as *Paul* and *crawl*; the same vowel sound as *look*; and the same vowel sound as *food*.

Read the words. The letters **oy** and **oi** stand for the vowel sounds in b**oy** and b**oi**l.

b**oy**   b**oi**l

Read each sentence. Then complete the word by adding <u>oi</u> or <u>oy</u>.

1. The little child cried with j_____ at the sight of the playful pups.

2. We will need more s_____l for the new plants.

3. The little b_____ laughed and ran toward his father.

4. Jen's new t_____ toppled off the table and broke.

5. Mom has to put _____l in her car.

6. The water for our tea will b_____l soon.

At Home: Have your child write sentences for some of the *oi* and *oy* words.

Sand Castle • **Book 1.5/Unit 6**   257

© Macmillan/McGraw-Hill

Write words from the box to complete the story.

grew	leave	toward	welcoming
circle	toppled	wreck	

1. The children _____ plants for their class.

2. Mike and Jen put some seeds in a _____ _____.

3. One tall plant _____ over.

4. Will the plant _____ their beautiful garden?

5. Let's turn all the plants _____ the sun now.

6. We will _____ the plants in the bright sunshine all week.

© Macmillan/McGraw-Hill

At Home: Have your child use some of the vocabulary words to tell what will happen next to the classroom garden.

As you read <u>Sand Castle</u>, fill in the Cause and Effect Chart.

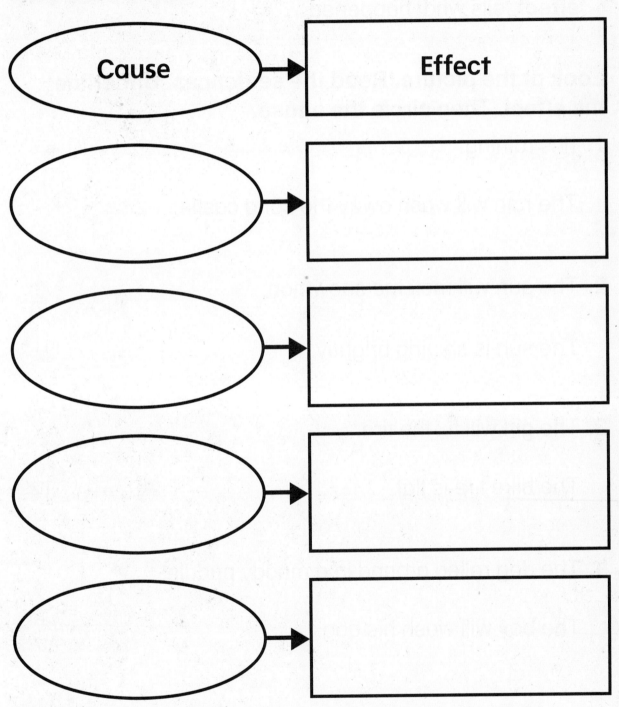

Cause

Effect

How does the Cause and Effect Chart help you better understand <u>Sand Castle</u>?

At Home: Have your child use the chart to retell the story.

Sand Castle • Book 1.5/Unit 6   259

The **cause** tells why something happened. The **effect** tells what happened.

Look at the picture. Read the sentences. Underline the effect. Then circle the cause.

1. It is raining.

   The rain will wash away the sand castle.

2. The sun will melt the snowman.

   The sun is shining brightly.

3. The girl will fix the tire.

   The bike tire is flat.

4. The dog rolled around in a muddy puddle.

   The boy will wash his dog.

© Macmillan/McGraw-Hill

At Home: Have your child identify a cause and effect situation at school or at home.

As I read, I will pay attention to patterns in the story.

	Meena looked out at the birds that had
8	come to her backyard.
12	"Look at how great they are," Meena said.
20	"I want them to stay and not fly away."
29	"Well, we can make a birdhouse," Mama
36	said. "It would be welcoming and then the
44	birds might not leave."
48	"That's a great idea," said Meena. "Let's
55	make it this afternoon."
59	Meena called her friends Wendy and Mark
66	to help. Soon Wendy and Mark came over.
74	Wendy took out paper and paints. Mark
81	took out wood and glue. And Meena put out
90	foil stickers. 92

Comprehension Check

1. Why does Meena want to build a birdhouse?

2. Do you think Meena, Wendy, and Mark are good friends?

	Words Read	−	Number of Errors	=	Words Correct Score
First Read		−		=	
Second Read		−		=	

At Home: Help your child read the passage, paying attention to the goal at the top of the page.

Use the <u>underlined</u> context clues to figure out the meaning of the word in bold letters. Then match the word to its meaning. Write the correct letter on the line.

a. moved round and round   **b.** came back

c. tapped gently   **d.** to keep safe

e. a bridge that can be raised and lowered

_ _ _ _

1. The royal family **returned** <u>home</u> <u>from</u> a <u>trip</u> to the countryside.   ___

_ _ _ _

2. The king, queen, and prince <u>crossed</u> <u>over</u> the **drawbridge** toward the <u>castle</u>.   ___

_ _ _ _

3. The happy queen kissed the prince and **patted** him <u>on</u> the <u>head</u>.   ___

_ _ _ _

4. <u>Water</u> from the <u>river</u> **swirled** in the <u>moat</u>.   ___

_ _ _ _

5. The <u>moat</u> and the <u>drawbridge</u> **protect** the <u>castle</u> from <u>strangers</u>.   ___

© Macmillan/McGraw-Hill

At Home: Tell your own story about a castle. Use the words *drawbridge* and *protect* in the story.

Name _____

Write a word from the box to complete each sentence. Then underline the letters in each word that stand for the vowel sound.

| toys | soil | coins | boy | broil |

_____

1. Jill got _____ on her jeans.

_____

2. Lee saved many _____ in his bank.

_____

3. The little _____ wanted to play on the slide.

_____

4. We will _____ our food for dinner tonight.

_____

5. The children looked at the _____ in the store.

© Macmillan/McGraw-Hill

At Home: Have your child think of other words with the *oi* and *oy* diphthongs and use one of them in a sentence.

Captions tell you facts about a photo or picture.

Read the captions. Then answer the questions.

On May 28, Paul and
Mom paint his bedroom.

1. Who is in the picture? _____

2. What are they doing? _____

3. What is the date? _____

On June 10, Pam and
Joy make a sand castle
at the beach.

4. Who are the children? _____

5. What are the children doing? _____

6. What is the date? _____

At Home: Help your child to make up some captions for
photographs in a family album.

Read the words.

The letters **oi** and **oy** stand for the sounds in

s**oi**l   t**oy**

Blend the sounds and say the word.
Write the word.
Draw a line to the picture that it describes.

1. b   oi   l _____

2. b   oy _____

3. t   oy _____

4. s   oi   l _____

At Home: Have your child change the first letter of one of the words to make a new word. Then have your child draw a picture of what the word names.

Name _____

Write the words from the box in the correct list.

bear	birds	space	cub	Earth

Animals

_____

_ _ _ _ _ _ _ _ _ _ _ _ _ _ _

_____

_ _ _ _ _ _ _ _ _ _ _ _ _ _ _

_____

Places

_____

_ _ _ _ _ _ _ _ _ _ _ _ _ _ _

_____

_ _ _ _ _ _ _ _ _ _ _ _ _ _ _

Use each word in a sentence.

across	circle	air

_____

_ _

_____

_ _

_____

_ _

_____

Circle the words that tell about the pictures.

I.

invisible bear

wild bear

2.

interesting laugh

interesting book

3.

only two eyes

only two mouths

4.

has been searching

has been welcoming

5.

toppled toward the boy

toppled toward the point

6.

leave enough room

grew enough

© Macmillan/McGraw-Hill